The TRUE Happiness Recipe

How to Stop Your Job from Killing You and Create Work – Life Harmony Every Day

By Will Marré

Foreword by Eric Severson, SVP of Talent at Gap

Part of the Food for Thought Series by

DEDICATION

This book is dedicated to my teachers.

Stephen Covey	Roy Baumeister
Jim Loehr	Joe Folkman
Jack Groppel	David Pink
Alan Fine	Carol Dweek
Chris Jordan	Martin Seligman
Raquel Malo	John Ratey
Tara Gidus	Daniel Friedland
Heather Fleming	Richard Wiseman
Florence Quinn	Nick Francis
Judith Stein	Bob Maurer
Monica Methany	Mihály Csíkszentmihályi
Peter Kaminsky	Herbert Benson
Mehmet Oz	Charlie Kim
Daniel Siegel	Eric Severson
Chris Osorio	

I thank each one of them for opening my mind, igniting my curiosity, and inspiring my life with new knowledge. Of course, they are not responsible for any of my conclusions, suggestions, or advice. If what you are about to read seems right or wrong, wise or wild, blame me.

JUST START!

Why I Want You to Read This Book and Change Your Life

For 30 years, I have helped people excel. It's not easy—excelling, that is. Since launching the American Dream Project (www.americandreamproject.org), I've come into contact with hundreds of thousands of people who want more than an average life. But like me, they are discovering that the requirements for success in the 21st century workplace are, at their core, unhealthy. Toxic, even.

Yet few of us do more than *wish* for our lives and our jobs to change. The self-help industry has misled us into thinking that there is a "secret" to positive thinking. The idea is that if we wish hard enough, we will attract the very outcomes we envision. Psychologist Richard Wiseman points out a tiny problem with this claim: experiments show that the exact opposite usually happens!

A research study at the University of California asked a group of students to visualize getting high grades. The result was they got over-confident, studied less, and got worse grades than their more realistic peers. Another study of NYU seniors who daily turned their imagination to "attracting" their dream jobs showed that they got fewer offers and lower salaries than students who scrambled for interviews, networked, and suffered through internships.

As the groundbreaking psychologist William James proposed over 100 years ago, positive action is far more powerful in igniting positive change than positive thinking. He was right.

And that's what this little book is about.

My cross-country American Dream Project journey has enabled me to see how the happiest people among us are those who take direct control over their jobs, their lives, their health, and their most important relationships. People who thrive take positive action in concrete steps, like following recipes for a delicious life. This book contains some of the best recipes I know to transform your life right now.

Oh, and it also has recipes for banana bread French toast, raw chocolate cake, and plenty of healthy, happy food.

By the time you're done with this book, you will see how the way we eat, the way we work, and the way we live are all connected. And you'll see how a few great recipes can transform your life.

Come with me. It's time to get cookin'.

Also by Will Marré:

Your Dreams on Fire

Save the World and Still Be Home For Dinner

Reclaiming Your American Dream PBS Documentary

TABLE OF CONTENTS

FOREWORD

By: Eric Severson, Senior Vice President, Talent, GAP

What is it about happiness that is at once so voraciously sought after—and yet so painfully elusive?

And why are so few of us living each moment to its fullest in the pursuit of both happiness and our best self?

The answer is stress, as Will Marré so eloquently observes in *The TRUE Happiness Recipe.* The truth is stress is literally killing us—and short-circuiting our potential for happiness along the way. But as Will also demonstrates so compellingly in this book, it doesn't have to be that way. And Will is a living, breathing example.

Will is one of those individuals who seems to "excel at everything." Here are just a handful of his remarkable achievements: co-founder and CEO of one of the most successful management training organizations of the 20th century; writer of an Emmy Award-winning documentary; founder of multiple non-profit organizations that have helped thousands of individuals and saved millions of acres within endangered ecosystems; author of several books; highly sought-after management consultant and coach, father of six happy and successful children; husband of a happy wife; and inhabitant of a mind and body that appear at least a decade younger than they are.

Why does it matter that Will has accomplished this

multitude of milestones?

Because he has done it all while cultivating happiness.

Will is the happiest and the least stressed, busy person I have ever encountered. Since beginning to work with him several years ago, I have marveled at his almost superhuman ability to tackle multiple goals in his business, personal, public, and community life without succumbing to anxiety and stress. Although in our work together at the Gap, Will has shared many of his secrets to happy, successful living with me, the beauty and genius of *The TRUE Happiness Recipe* is that it synthesizes in a *single* volume decades of wisdom, insight, and knowledge from the art and science of human high performance.

In our work together to create *Performance for Life*, Gap's program to drive organizational performance through proven practices for maximizing employee well-being, Will and I have collaborated on something that is almost unheard of in corporate America: teaching employees how to be "better at everything" by being well. Whether teaching employees how to break destructive habits like multi-tasking, how to eat mindfully, or how to integrate stretching breaks into their workday, our work has been focused on building habits for successful, stress-free living. In short, we are teaching happiness.

One of the things I admire most about Will is his ability to translate powerful insights from psychology, medicine, nutrition, exercise physiology, neuroscience, and other scientific domains into practical solutions that REAL people can easily integrate into their daily lives. Will is the master of "good habits," understanding intuitively how to create rituals for success in life that not only work, but can be readily implemented and sustained. This is what makes *The TRUE Happiness Recipe* such a treasure trove. It is literally a manual for happy living.

In the course of developing *Performance for Life* at Gap, my team and I have absorbed literally hundreds of books, articles, and lectures on the art and science of human high performance and well-being. Every week, I recommend one or more of these resources to friends or colleagues looking to improve the performance and well-being of themselves, their families, or their teams. Yet, as powerful as these resources are, I have never encountered one that sets forth in such clear, effective, step-by-step language the *formula* for sustained happiness and success. Will's "cookbook" for happiness, filled with soon-to-be-classic "recipes" like "Super Flow," "Good Morning Harmony," and "Unplug, Rest and Recharge," applies the emerging science of human habit formation to help users create formulas for change that are as simple and straightforward as following the recipes in a cookbook. Mastering the recipes may take practice, but anyone, anywhere, can do them.

The one thing I have most lamented in my own study of human success and happiness has been the dearth of resources devoted to *converting* the burgeoning knowledge of this subject into *practical solutions* that busy, stressed-out people (the ones who really need it) can actually apply to their daily lives. *The TRUE Happiness Recipe* is the resource I—and anyone who has ever felt the debilitating impact of stress—have been waiting for.

Happiness, I've discovered, is highly personal. No one can make you happy. But with the right recipes, you can certainly cook up more happiness. I reflected on this recently as my partner and I drove to Cape Cod to join my family for the celebration of my parents' 50th wedding anniversary. As we savored hamburgers, watermelon, cupcakes, and each others' company around a long wooden table, surrounded with red, white and blue decorations, I could not help but smile as I reflected on Will's recipes for a happy life—and took pride in knowing that at least on this day, my family and I were "top chefs." My hope for you is that through the wisdom in *The TRUE Happiness Recipe* you and your loved ones will share in our discovery.

Eric Severson

Part 1: Getting Ready to Cook

We Already Know How to Be Happy

Don't eat junk food.

Don't think junk thoughts.

Don't do junk work.

Don't turn your life to junk.

Just don't.

You certainly don't have to. Science has revealed more about the connections between health, happiness, and work than we've ever known in history. And that new knowledge has appeared just in time. Because we are starving.

Starving? Yes. Not so much for bodily nourishment, but for soul nourishment. Though our cupboards may be full, our *lives* often feel empty. Rushed. Unfulfilled. In our pursuit of abundant food—and other "necessities"—we've pushed our happiness into the sub-basement of our awareness.

And we're starving for it. In a way no bacon double-cheeseburger can satisfy.

The crazy part is it doesn't have to be this way. In many

ways, life today is great. Astonishingly so. Our average life span is close to eighty. A hundred years ago, it was fifty. Today, we expect to raise all our children to adulthood. A hundred years ago, we would have lost two or three children to diseases or accidents. We now have indoor plumbing, antibiotics, instant knowledge at our fingertips, and movie theaters in our living rooms. The comforts and securities we enjoy today are so much greater than in the "good old days" that any of our great grandparents would have traded places with us in a New York nanosecond.

Yet we suffer from ten times the depression we had in 1960. And the renowned Cooper Clinic forecasts that 52% of people working in management will die from diseases caused by job stress. Yes, that's death from work. Gulp.

What's going on? Simply this: Now that we have tamed the dangers of nature, we have unleashed the demons of our own natures. Most of our suffering today is caused by our choices. Our habits—the way we work, live, and eat—are making us sick. And miserable. And that's just insane.

We need new recipes for living... and a new approach to working.

Cooking Up Some Happiness

The last thing I ever thought I would do is write a recipe book. After all, I barely cook. So this is an unexpected turn. I've spent my career coaching executives and leaders. It's been good work. Most of the people I work with shower daily and don't physically assault me. So I count my blessings.

I've even learned a thing or two along the way.

I began my profession nearly thirty years ago, when I stumbled into a seminar called "The Seven Habits of Highly Effective People." It jacked up my imagination about what was possible for human beings. It was my first formal introduction to the power of habits—how they are within our control, and how they can spark a wildfire of positive change in our lives.

Thinking about the power of habit became a bit of an obsession for me. I tracked down Stephen Covey, the seminar leader, quit my job, packed my family in our Oldsmobile station wagon, and moved a thousand miles so I could convince him to resign his professorship and start a leadership training business with me. It wasn't easy, but I was very clear that this was what I was designed to do. It felt like a calling. My TRUE work (I'll tell you what makes work TRUE later).

It was then I began my deep dive into the field of work and happiness.

But wait, what's that got to do with a cookbook?

Well, life is long and full of unexpected experiences. Some are nice surprises, others are about as welcome as an armed home invasion. I've had my share of both. But let me tell you about one very happy surprise.

About ten years ago, I was invited to join the Advisory Board of the Human Performance Institute, a premier center devoted to translating scientific research into practical steps people can take to thrive under stressful conditions. The Institute was founded by a renowned sports psychologist, Dr. Jim Loehr, and a leading exercise physiologist, Dr. Jack Groppel. Over the years, these two men and their team have helped sixteen athletes become number one in the world and scores of others win Olympic medals. Clients range from tennis players to racecar drivers, from professional football players to chess champions. The Institute also trains Special Forces, SWAT teams, and business leaders. Any pros who need to be at their best under conditions of immense stress.

As you might imagine, I've met and worked with some pretty amazing people. People who've accomplished astonishing things. And yet I've come to realize that *we all* struggle with the same issues. Whether we're striving to win an NBA Championship or simply struggling with the daily stress of paying the bills, we all yearn for one elusive state of being. Happiness.

I know *I* did. When I met Jim and Jack, I was just emerging from a major life disappointment and was convinced I needed to do something new to avoid getting caught up in the swirling drain of my old habits. Fortunately, I had an epiphany. Jim and Jack had fused all the "psychology of happiness" tools I had been using for decades with a profound understanding of the *physical forces* our bodies exert on our brains and emotions. In doing so, they had created a truly integrated process that *measurably increases* both health and happiness.

That opened a door for me. I began to interview experts and scores of people whose lives have been transformed by making changes to their daily routines. I asked about what they *do* and what and when they eat. I hired a research team and published over a hundred tips and techniques to increase human vitality and happiness.

But the greatest thing was, I was able to get results for myself. By melding the wisdom of nutrition and exercise with my professional understanding of how to develop self-empowering habits, I was able to tangibly strengthen my own capacity for happiness. I also permanently changed the way I work each day.

I followed simple, concrete steps and my life got better. Hugely so. Hallelujah.

The great news is that it's not rocket science.

The Happiness Lie

Why is unhappiness so rampant in a world where we have so much?

Maybe it's because we've been taught that our happiness is largely out of our control. We believe that events just happen. When they're *good* events, we feel happy; when they're *bad* events, we feel sad or frustrated. Unhappiness is just a natural reaction to things going badly. Right?

Wrong. That's a big fat lie.

We now know a whole lot about what creates human happiness. Much more than we knew a few years ago. Hundreds of scientific studies on happiness-related topics have been published in the past ten years. In fact, a new field called Positive Psychology has sprung up recently and it's devoted to one pursuit only: discovering what we can do to make us happy—not just for a moment or two, but day in and day out, at home, at work, and at play. This is what I call TRUE happiness (again, more on that soon).

So What Is Happiness?

Well, we could devote an entire book to exploring that idea, but let's keep it simple. Science has defined two key dimensions of happiness. First, it's an inner feeling of contentment, a calm sense that things are good right now. Second, it's an optimism that things are likely to get better. Sounds like a great dinner to me—that satisfying feeling after a tasty main course when you're anticipating the delight of a special dessert.

So if happiness is so simple, why does it seem so elusive? Well, for years serious, hardworking high-achievers acted as if happiness was for sissies. Their thinking seemed to be that people who made serious money and had a serious impact on the world should set aside their happiness for big, important goals. Wrapped up in this view is the belief that life goals are best attained by brute effort and personal sacrifice.

This kind of thinking is rampant among top leaders and entrepreneurs. How do I know this? Because I coach these people. I see how they struggle with the disconnect between success and happiness. First, they think that goal achievement and more money should make them happy. When it doesn't, they dismiss happiness as something whimsical and extraneous. Something for human resource people and soul-searching ex-hippies to worry about.

But happiness is a lot more *real* and basic than that. And a lot more important. We now know, for instance, that people who are mostly happy live longer, have better relationships, get more education, make more money, recognize more opportunity, and actually have more enjoyable success.

Perhaps we got off track because for a long time psychologists believed it was foolish to pursue happiness directly. In fact, they often taught that focusing on being happy would make you frustrated and *un*happy. We were told that happiness was simply a byproduct of a well-lived life, coupled with a large dose of luck. Fortunately for all of us, that's dead wrong. It turns out that Thomas Jefferson was right. The *pursuit* of happiness is the best strategy for life.

That's because happiness is a cause as well as an effect. Feelings of happiness inspire us to make wise choices that help us achieve worthwhile goals, develop satisfying relationships, and seek fulfillment. Of course, those are the very things that contribute to feeling happier. So the happiness cycle, in which happiness *causes* happiness, can be an extremely potent force in our lives. And we now know that we can accelerate our own cycle of happiness. We can deliberately increase both our happiness and our *capacity to be happy*. And we know how to do it. It's not about the events that happen *out there*, it's about the choices we make *in here*.

Inner choices are the key to TRUE happiness.

Better Choices

So, are you ready to get on the happy train?

Well, not so fast. Making choices that bring us happiness has a *lot* to do with how we feel. Both emotionally and physically.

The Chemistry of Happiness

What we're learning today is that body chemistry is tied to happiness in an endless feedback loop. The way we feel and live affects our chemistry, and our chemistry affects the way we feel and live. One example of this is the chemistry of stress.

Stress has become a dominant force in modern life. But it's not just a mental/emotional concern; it's a biochemical event. Stress *changes our body chemistry*, which changes our mood and health. Which, in turn, changes our behavior. Which, in turn, changes our body chemistry. Which changes our mood and health... You get the idea.

Of course, stress is part of life. Some stress we cannot avoid. A hundred and fifty years ago we were stressed by fires, famine, deadly childhood diseases, and a host of forces we had no control over. Today, it's different. Much of our stress is psychological, rather than physical.

The stress hothouse of today's era is the workplace. Recent research confirms that people who work in a hostile work environment where they feel manipulated, threatened, or coerced to obey orders and achieve goals are 2.4 times more likely to die sooner than people who work in more inspiring circumstances.

Even if you don't work in a downright hostile workplace, plain old management incompetence may be pushing your stress level beyond the tipping point. Workplaces where people are chronically overloaded, confused about priorities, unable to use or develop their strengths, or kept in the dark about important decisions all generate performance-killing, health-destroying stress.

The sad part is, all this work stress is unnecessary. Stupid, even.

What we're learning now is that it's *inspiration*, not stress, that drives results. One of the most extensive long-term studies on work success was performed by my colleagues, Joe Folkman and Jack Zenger. Working with over 100 global enterprises, they found that extraordinary business results are driven primarily by *inspiring* (not browbeating) employees to strive. Alas, this same research also revealed that inspiration is the least common leadership capability. Not too surprising.

What's this got to do with our health and happiness?

Plenty.

In the old days, most stress-producing challenges flared up suddenly and were over just as fast. Today's psychological stress is relentless. Never-ending. We're tapped into the stress machine 24/7. It's not only our jobs that are killing us. We also generate gobs of stress through troubled relationships, uncertain finances, raising children in an unsafe world, and even loneliness.

Humans are not designed to deal with relentless stress. Not physically, not emotionally, not mentally. So it makes us sick. How? Under stress, a substance called cortisol is released in our bloodstream. It's like homemade Red Bull. For about twenty minutes, it's a good thing. It makes us alert, focused, and ready to tackle whatever is threatening us. But today's "threats" don't go away in twenty minutes. So neither does the cortisol. And if cortisol remains in our bloodstream too long, it begins to wear us down from the inside out.

Today, the levels of cortisol in the typical American remain high throughout the day and into the evening. The result— it's killing us. Here's a list of all the bad things elevated levels of cortisol cause.

Cortisol Overdose

1. Impaired cognition -------- Bad judgment
2. Suppressed thyroid -------- Quick fatigue
3. Blood sugar imbalance ---- Diabetes
4. Decreased bone density -- Brittle bones
5. Decreased muscle mass --- Weakness & low energy
6. High blood pressure ------- Heart attack & stroke
7. Abdominal fat --------------- Arterial disease
8. Lower Immunity ----------- Colds, flu, infection
9. Inflammation --------------- Everything bad

So let's be clear about this: the way we live and work creates stress. Stress triggers the release of cortisol. Cortisol attacks our health, our mood, our judgment, and our energy level, making us very unhappy. And it's getting worse. An occupational health study recently confirmed that most new jobs being created today are loaded with stress accelerators such as high demands, low pay, low control, and little security. It's no wonder that a new university study reveals that stress levels have increased 22% in the past 25 years! That is a five-alarm fire!

Yet we *can* put out this fire of stress. Our daily life and our daily work are much more under our control than we believe. That's what the recipes in the second part of this book are all about. They'll give you a fire hose to beat back the flames of stress. They'll help you continuously recharge your happiness.

It all starts with food.

How Food Matters

Nutritional science tells us that food and happiness are embraced in a dance. Again, it's a biochemical thing. Did you know, for example, that your entire day can be impacted by what you eat or don't eat in the first thirty minutes? Eating in the first half-hour flips the switch to your body's engine room. It only takes fifty to a hundred calories to ignite your biological horsepower. When you do, wham! The lights come on. Your engine revs. Your mind-body gets ready to rumble.

On the other hand, when you eat nothing, your mind-body doesn't fully awaken. Your metabolism stays in idle mode, conserving energy, afraid it may be deprived of food all day. This can actually put a limit on your energy throughout the entire day, even *after* you eat. Imagine trying to coax your mind-body into being present and loving for your family send-off, or alert and focused for a high-stakes business meeting, when you have no fuel in your tank.

It doesn't take a Hungry Man's Special to crank the body's engine, either. A few nuts and half an apple will do. If that doesn't work, a fully loaded small latte can do the trick. Why are fruits and nuts better than a Pop-tart, or latte better than black coffee? One reason is that a bit of high-quality protein, as found in nuts or milk, helps slow down the conversion of food to sugar (glucose), so we get a nice sustained pipeline of energy, instead of a gusher followed by a drought.

On the other hand, when we chow down on simple sugars or simple carbohydrates—a bagel and jam, for example—our body quickly converts it all to glucose that stimulates our insulin system. Which soon makes us feel tired and blah. Sugar rush followed by a crash. All from a friendly-looking bagel.

Now, I don't want to bog you down with nutritional science, because I don't want you to sink into a mental coma. After all, this is a book about happiness, right? But a little bit of understanding about how moods and foods interact is important here, so hang in there for just a minute longer. I'm going to share one more nutritional truth that will help you make the chemical connection.

Here it is:

The foundation of personal vitality is a strong and consistent level of glucose throughout the day and evening. A steady glucose level combats the five assassins of happiness, which are:

1. Fatigue
2. Anxiety
3. Confusion
4. Isolation
5. Cynicism

Each of these five assassins attacks our resilience, creativity, open-mindedness, friendliness, and presence, which are the major drivers of happiness.

Again: *what* we eat and *when* we eat is crucial for our mind-body to feel positive and optimistic. And these feelings are the touchstones of happiness.

Food and happiness. Dance partners. See? That's why we can't talk about one without talking about the other.

Healthy Food and Fads

So how does this information translate into an eating plan?

Over the past ten years, I have talked to and worked with many nutritionists, and I've found the best ones are not "food fanatics." I've also lived through many waves of food fads. All-meat diets. All-liquid diets. All-fruit diets. *No-fruit* diets. Low-carb diets. Vegan, vegetarian, pescatarian, flexitarian... The truth is, nutrition is personal and complex. Everything we eat interacts with our body chemistry. But each of us has a *chemistry that's unique.*

So to say there is one ultimate and perfect diet for everyone is foolishly arrogant. I respect people who thrive on veganism and avoid gluten, lactose, or any food that makes them feel bad. I also respect people who feel good including meat in their diet. In fact, that is the crux of my approach. I don't so much subscribe to a diet dogma, as I ask people "How do you feel? How do you look? What do you eat?"

If you are energetic all day, feel healthy, and are within five pounds of your ideal weight—*and* you are over 30—you are probably eating pretty well. (If you are under age 25, you may be living on fried chicken, beer, and ice cream and still be looking and feeling pretty good. Youth can mask stupid eating... for a while.) If, on the other hand, you feel exhausted at the end of an average day and/or avoid looking into full-length mirrors, you are probably not eating well.

Then What's the Right Way to Eat?

Well, not fad diets. Most fad diets actually destroy the willpower needed to stay on them. How? By failing to promote the positive moods necessary to optimism and happiness. And that's a critical piece. To consistently feel good, we must eat good food. But if we don't get positive feelings from our food choices, we most likely won't eat what's good for us. Not for the long term.

The most universal advice I can give you is this: eat real food, not processed, chemical-injected, pseudo-food. Our bodies were not designed to be chemical processing plants. We are *always* healthier and happier when we eat delicious—even *rich*—food made from real ingredients. As long as we keep the quantities sane.

Why do we eat so much garbage, then? Well, we all have relationships with food, as we do with romantic partners. Some of us have promiscuous appetites. We lust after instant pleasure, telling ourselves that *real* food requires too much commitment, or that all nutritious food tastes like tofu. But the truth is, great food is never boring. The best food is gorgeous to look at, intoxicating to smell, and delightful to taste. It also builds healthy bodies and stimulates happy brains.

Real Food Equals Real Flavor

I recently started working with the delightful European chef nutritionist Florence Quinn (*http://www.aboutfood.biz*), who generously shares many of her own recipes later in the book. She is an evangelist for flavor, as well as health. She told me, "If I were to tell my clients that they will have to eat brown rice and broccoli for the rest of their lives, the chances of making a successful lifestyle change are slim, but if I suggest they add a few crumbs of blue cheese, aged parmesan, or bacon to electrify a salad or a full-grain pasta, it will go a long way to entice and satisfy all their senses." Cheese, bacon... sounds good to me.

Florence builds on Peter Kaminsky's idea of "flavor per calorie," pointing out that our taste buds are designed to somersault with pleasure in response to interesting combinations of sour and bitter tastes that have nearly disappeared from our diet.

She observes that today, sadly, many people don't know how to appreciate real food and don't take the time to really taste. Instead, the fake convenience of manufactured food makes us think that bland and muted flavors are normal. So many of us are now addicted to the gobs of sugar, salt, and fat injected into processed foods to make them palatable.

Florence is passionate about "farm to table" eating. She believes in cooking with love, buying the freshest and best ingredients you can find (quality over quantity), constantly trying bold new ingredients, sharing meals with friends, and eating food that nourishes both body and soul.

How we eat is just as important as what we eat. Raquel Malo and Tara Gidus, nutritionists at the Human Performance Institute, taught me that the key is to never be *really* full or *really* hungry. Always feel satisfied—no hunger or cravings—but never feel stuffed. You can do this by eating natural, real food, like you'll find in the recipes in this book. The key is to eat three right-sized meals and three to four small snacks each day.

The point I want you to remember is this: *what* we eat, *how* we eat, and *when* we eat is absolutely critical to both our sense of well-being and our minute-to-minute energy for living. And that translates directly into our feelings of happiness. Happiness as each of us individually experiences it.

Our Mind-Body

We have been led to believe that the three-pound nerve-blob inside our skull is a master computer that sends its commands to the body below our necks. We think our bodies are simply flesh, blood, and bones. But neuroscientists now have a new understanding. Turns out, we are one big brain. Or, better put, one integrated mind-body.

As you were developing in the womb, brain cells were being distributed *throughout your body*. Large clusters of them surround your heart, where you have sensations of love and trust and "heartbreak." Your intestines maintain a great campsite of brain cells that are directly connected to your feelings of intuition. A "gut" response to people and events is exactly that.

Our brains and bodies are one integrated system. How we treat our body, especially through diet and exercise, directly impacts our brain's ability to guide and direct our behavior.

The Other Half of Happiness

Are we really what we eat? To a major extent, yes. What we eat is crucial to our health and vitality. Food is our primary fuel for living, loving, laughing, and achieving. It has a monumental effect on our attitudes, emotions, and energy levels, as well as our brain's higher functions. Good food leads to happy brains.

And happy brains lead to happy thoughts.

But of course, that's only part of the picture. The healthiest, most nutrient-rich brain in the world cannot deliver happiness if our behavior is doggedly working against us. To be happy, we must also *act* in ways that lead to happiness.

I know this may seem self-evident, but as a culture, we have adopted many behavior patterns that seem precisely engineered to produce *un*happiness. We indulge in these patterns, day after day, and then wonder why the end result is emptiness, frustration, and anxiety.

Some of these behavior patterns revolve around eating badly, such as:
- eating big, heavy meals two or three times a day
- eating on the run
- eating fake, heavily processed foods
- eating compulsively as a form of "entertainment"

Other behavior patterns revolve around pulling our attention *away* from the things we deeply value and investing it in things that make us miserable. Just a few examples of this are:

- doing work that offers little meaning or satisfaction
- working hard without using our talents, strengths, or creativity
- working for mean or incompetent bosses
- working long hours at the job, week after week
- answering emails on evenings and weekends, instead of spending time with the people we love and enjoy
- staying hunched over a computer monitor for endless hours without moving our bodies
- taking our work home with us
- zoning out over television, instead of pursuing our passions or engaging with friends
- spending all our money on *things,* instead of on experiences and people

When our behavior diverts us *away* from inherently rewarding pursuits and *toward* inherently unrewarding ones, we become unhappy. Period. Yet many of us try to believe otherwise. We think we can continue to devote most of our attention to things we don't deeply value, yet somehow *feel* deeply happy. It's crazy. Happiness doesn't work that way.

If we want to be happy, we need to support our happiness with our daily choices. That means we need to make sure our (1) body chemistry and (2) behavior are *working together* in ways that lead to feelings of contentment and optimism. When either of these elements is off, we destroy the fundamental conditions on which happiness is built. When both of these elements are working together, though, TRUE happiness can settle into our lives naturally and effortlessly. It is no longer something we have to chase, like greyhounds chasing a mechanical rabbit.

Fortunately, there is a single solution to getting both our chemistry and our behavior working for us, instead of against us. It comes down to one simple word:

Habit

The Power of Habits

If you desire to feel happy more often—and who doesn't—the fastest way is to change your habits.

I know what you're thinking —"Yeah, yeah, that may be true, but changing habits is hard."

No, it isn't. We *tell* ourselves that changing our habits is hard. But it's easy. In fact, changing our habits is the easiest way to change our lives. Small adjustment, big payoff. New habits can even be fun and pleasant. Who knew?

Why do I say changing habits is easy? Well, you see, our brains are *designed* for automatic thinking. They love efficiency and repetition. They try to conserve the bulk of their computing power to run our bodies, direct our attention, and solve new challenges. So in order to operate efficiently, our brains are always generating programmed responses to familiar situations. They write these programs quickly and try to engrain them with the least amount of effort.

Habits Have Three Parts

There are three parts to habits: a trigger, an automatic response, and a payoff.

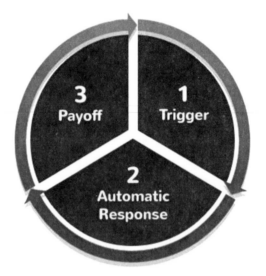

Let's say, for example, you have a childhood fear of snakes that you've never reprogrammed. Today, when you see a snake on a hiking trail (even a harmless one), you head for the hills. That's a habit. The **trigger** is seeing the snake. The **automatic response** is to flee, and the **reward** is a feeling of relief and safety.

All of us have thousands of habits. Some are positive; many are negative. For instance, your brother-in-law might trigger the same automatic response as a snake. This is not a very helpful reaction at family gatherings. The point is, we are biologically wired to create habits, and most of them are invisible to us. As long as they *remain* invisible, they control our happiness.

It's simple. Our responses to the thousands of triggers we encounter every day set off chain reactions of thoughts, emotions, and behaviors, generating payoffs that we believe are the best we can hope for.

Understanding *payoffs* is critical to changing habits.

Three Types of Payoff

Payoffs come in three flavors.

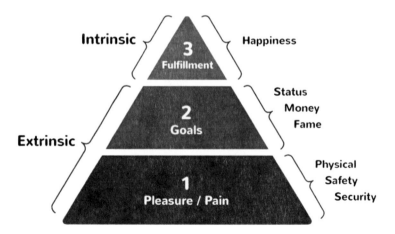

1. **Pleasure/Pain.** Achieving pleasure and avoiding pain is the kind of payoff a baby seeks. It's infantile. Literally. Babies are driven to demand full bellies and clean diapers. When they don't get them, they respond by crying and fussing. This behavior is cute when a baby does it. Coming from an adult, it's called bullying and manipulating, and it's not so cute.

   Yet many adults are driven, on a daily basis, to pursue infantile payoffs of maximizing pleasure and minimizing pain. If you are driven too much by this type of payoff, you'll find yourself addicted to easy ways to increase pleasure, such as sex, drugs, rock 'n roll recklessness, or cheez curlz. You may also try to avoid the pain of responsibility, challenging work, deep relationships, and other high-functioning choices. We all know people like this.

2. **Goals.** The second level of payoff is adolescent. Operating at this level, we form habits that we believe will bring us money, fame, and status from doing what others expect of us and the goals they reward us for achieving. Peer pressure plays in heavily here. Social research confirms that most adults are driven by payoffs at this level. When we chase this kind of payoff, we may be considered responsible and successful by others... but *we* may not be very happy. At least, not very often.

   The reason is simple. Extrinsic payoffs that only satisfy our physical needs or salve our emotional self-doubts do not make us happy. Most jobs are designed to motivate us with extrinsic rewards of money and status. But no amount of either really makes us happy. Happiness requires a third level of payoff.

3. **Fulfillment.** The third, highest level of payoff is a positive feeling that we are becoming our best, most authentic self. Call it self-actualization. Feelings of fulfillment and optimism arise in us when we believe we are living a meaningful life that follows our own best personal blueprint. This is TRUE happiness.

   Now here is the interesting part. The happiest people literally have it all. They frequently experience level 1 pleasures—good food, good drink, good chocolate, pleasures that ignite the senses. They also achieve important level 2 goals and have enough money to feel secure. But most importantly, they are also working toward becoming their best, most authentic self (level 3).

The secret to building habits that lead to happiness, then, is to change the payoff.

The Payoff Is the Critical Element

Often when we change habits, we do so to escape pain and increase pleasure. In other words, we aim for level 1 payoffs. And that's an inadequate life strategy. It ultimately works against our happiness. How so? Well, in order for pleasure to give us a buzz, it needs to constantly increase in intensity and novelty. That's just how our brains work. For example, we quickly get used to five-star hotels if we stay in them for ten nights running. Trying to constantly outdo past pleasures makes us both kinky and crazy—we've all seen rich Hollywood stars who act out this futile scenario. Trying to escape pain is also fruitless. It causes us to duck from important challenges and to try to control the uncontrollable. That never works in the long run.

We also try to change habits by aiming for level 2 payoffs— more status, more stuff, more success, or a feeling of doing what's right or expected. This type of habit change is difficult. It requires toxic amounts of self-control, and often fails. Many of us spend a lifetime trying to change our habits by aiming for level 2 payoffs. Sometimes we are successful, by a sheer act of will. Often, we're not. Either way, we are usually disappointed.

That's because we lack an *emotional commitment* to change the habit. This is a crucial point: in order to really change, our commitment needs to be based on personal values that we are *emotionally committed* to. Just trying to change because we *think* it's good for us (like dieting) or are *ethically* committed to it (like stopping flirting because we're in a committed relationship) is not enough. We only change our habits *for good* when our emotions climb on board. We have to *want* to change more than whatever payoff we get from not changing.

The acclaimed actor Robert Downey, Jr. went to jail twice,

rather than stop his drug addiction. Then he met an amazing woman, who gave him an ultimatum: "Me or drugs... no excuses." He knew what he really wanted on an emotional level. He quit drugs and became Ironman. He famously said, "Changing isn't hard; it's *deciding* to change that is." Successful change must engage your emotions.

Here's where things gets interesting. Our emotions actually become *easier* to engage when we aim for level 3 payoffs. Change then becomes *much* less laborious and *much* more doable. Why? Because all of us, on a deep emotional level, want to become the best and most authentic version of ourselves. So when we aim for payoffs that reflect our deepest values, bringing us closer to the best life we can imagine, our emotions kick in big-time.

And our emotions are what make new habits *stick*.

So it turns out that habits that lead to true happiness are much easier to adopt than habits that lead only to fake happiness. OK, that's a wow!

It gets even better.

Discovering the "Recipe" for Success

A few years ago, I created an assessment tool that measures people's sustained happiness: *The Dreamlife Assessment*. Over 26,000 people have taken it. (You can take it yourself at *http://www.thoughtrocket.com/true-happiness*). This is what I've learned empirically: people

31

who feel happy a great deal of the time do indeed create special habits for themselves. They are very aware of what triggers negative responses in them, and they avoid or transcend these situations. They intentionally develop positive routines in response to negative triggers, and they often seek higher-level (level 3) payoffs.

This is exciting news. It means that if we intentionally change our habits, we *can* increase our happiness. And it turns out, we *can* change our habits. How?

Well, I pondered that question for a while and had an insight. Not surprisingly, it circled back to food again. I thought about the way we create new habits in the kitchen. It's not by following abstract advice. No, we do it by following concrete, easy-to-do steps.

Recipes

As I thought back on my experiences helping people make breakthroughs in their *lives* and careers, I realized the same thing was true in those arenas. No matter what kind of change we're talking about, people respond to concrete tips, techniques, and know-how. Follow-able steps. As UCLA psychologist Bob Mauer taught me, our confidence grows when we have simple, fail-safe formulas to follow.

Recipes.

Just as good health comes from yummy food ingredients combined and prepared in a specific way, so too does human happiness. Happiness and fulfillment are inner feelings cooked up by our brains when our *lives* follow certain recipes.

By adopting new recipes for living and working, we can create new habits, easily and painlessly. We can change the trigger (sometimes), we can change our response (always), and we can change the payoff (always).

Pretty awesome.

That's why I've decided to put the meat of this book in the form of recipes. Some of them are recipes for eating; some are recipes for living and working. All are crucial.

Two Kinds of Recipes

In the recipe part of this book, I will take you through a day in a life of happiness, from morning until night. I will give you delicious, healthy recipes for snacks and meals, from the super simple to the more complex. I will also give you *recipes for happiness* that you can use from the moment you awaken until your head hits the pillow at night.

Just like my good food recipes, these happiness recipes are ready to cook. Each one is short and is combined with an action habit. The action habit is crucial. Nothing happens without action. Sure, healthy thinking is important, but it changes nothing on its own. Action changes everything—not random action, of course, but action that follows the science of human growth.

33

Positive Psychology has cracked open the mystery of human transformation. We now *know* how certain people make amazing transformations from obesity to fitness, dropout to billionaire, junkie to super mom. And that knowledge is embedded in the recipes in this book—both the food recipes and the thought-behavior recipes.

On the food side, you'll see that we've provided solutions for all your meals and snacks. You will notice that we favor totally yummy food, not just flax and lentils. My recipes deliver tasty food that even a four-year-old would want to steal off your plate. Some of these gooey and delicious items, like banana bread French toast with ice cream, are calorie-dense. Yet you will discover that if you eat them at the right time, with the right companion food, and in the right quantity, you can celebrate one of life's most sensuous pleasures without becoming obese.

On the behavior side, you'll see that we've taken the guesswork out of happiness. By combining carefully selected "ingredients" according to a formula, you can cook up "happiness meals and snacks" each day. Of course, these "happy meals" have nothing to do with toys and junk food. Rather, they are routines you can integrate into the flow of your daily life, from morning until night. They will not only bring you pleasure in the moment but also promote long-term, positive feelings of well-being, optimism, creativity, confidence, clarity, and purpose.

Just like good, tasty food recipes, these happiness recipes are well tested. Neurotechnology now enables us to look directly at human brains as their owners engage in specific habits. The result? We can now see *actual biological evidence* that these happiness recipes strengthen the areas of the brain that cope with stress, reframe negative experiences, and generate positive moods.

This is a major breakthrough. We are seeing what we previously could not see. That means we no longer have to wonder what makes us feel happy and fulfilled. Rather, we can simply follow recipes that bring more peace and contentment into our lives. The bonus—it's not hard to do. In fact, you already know how to do it. But now, instead of experiencing only random blips of happiness, you can take direct shortcuts to bliss.

All you need to do is follow the recipes.

Use Both Types of Recipe

It's important to use both kinds of recipes in this book. Why? Well, we've already seen how food and happiness are joined at the hip. But here's something that may surprise you. It also turns out that food plays a critical role in changing your habits.

How? There is one prime factor that makes it either easy or nearly impossible to change a habit. You already know what it is. Willpower. My friend, Dr. Jim Loehr, describes willpower as the energy you are willing to invest in personal change. And now we know what the greatest driver of willpower energy is...

...Wait for it....

It's our glucose level.

Huh?

That's right, our glucose level. Have you ever tried to avoid eating the hot rolls and butter they bring you at restaurants when you are starving? Good luck. Have you ever tried to remain calm when you're hungry and you're being nagged and nagged?

No, when we are hungry, we are irritable and self-indulgent. And when we are overfull—like we feel after Thanksgiving dinner—we are dull and unambitious. It turns out our willpower is directly affected by either edgy hunger or dull over-fullness. That means that if we spend our days cycling up the mountain of hunger or coasting down the slope of numbing fullness, our greatest power— the power to choose—is severely handicapped. That's because, as research psychologist Roy Baumeister tells us, the mental/emotional work of self-control and decision-making requires energy.

So eating the right foods at the right times is a major key to fueling the willpower needed to stick to a new habit until it becomes automatic.

See how it works? Our two types of recipe mutually support each other to produce the conditions in which happiness blooms naturally and without arduous effort.

What, Exactly, Are We Cooking Up Here?

And so what are we ultimately trying to accomplish here? How, exactly will you benefit from these recipes? Well, they're all about the third kind of payoff. Level 3 stuff. The recipes in this book—*both* kinds of recipe—are geared toward supporting you in becoming the best version of yourself that you can possibly be. That means truly fulfilled, deeply rewarded, and making an authentic contribution to the world.

That's what TRUE Happiness is all about.

And it all starts with your work.

You'll notice that I've centered my recipes for happiness around your workday. Why? Because work dominates our feelings about happiness. There's nothing wrong about that--quite the contrary, in fact. Work is tremendously important to our inner life. We are designed to be productive. In fact, studies show that the leading "cause" of premature death among males is retiring. It's more predictive of health failure than smoking or obesity. When we lose the sense of focus and purpose that work provides our souls begin to wither.

Though it may seem that I've been focusing on the negative aspects of work, the truth is that work *should* be a source of meaning, growth, and yes, even identity. That's true whether our primary work is raising children, painting pictures, or running a company. Our work is not separate from our lives and our relationships. It is part of a seamlessly interwoven fabric. In fact, our most fundamental source of fulfillment is the value we create for others. That's our true work.

For most of us, the problem is not work itself, but how we work. For the past few decades, American business has been obsessed with efficiency, process, and productivity. Do more with less. Root out waste. Work harder. Work longer. Avoid risk. Benchmark. Do what everyone else is doing, only do it better. Become world-class at blah, blah, blah. The result is rigid business processes that create stress-infused workplaces, where people serve the system instead of the system serving people. Work is reduced to a data-driven "assembly line" that extinguishes initiative by reducing anyone's individual impact. This is a talent killer, a completely out-of-gas way to run a business. It's killing companies and it's killing people.

The truth is that being productive doesn't have to be stressful and soul-draining. In fact, just the opposite is true. We work better when we are happy and whole. Some courageous companies have started to show us how this works.

For example, Charlie Kim, a friend of mine who founded Next Jump, a high-tech enterprise, is a true warrior in creating a non-stress-driven workplace. Next Jump's headquarters is in a Manhattan midrise where he converted lots of expensive office space into a fun, state-of-the-art gym filled not only with weights and treadmills, but also climbing walls, a batting cage, and a golf simulator.

Charlie retains some of New York's finest trainers and rewards employees for exercising during the workday. He has an on-site nutritionist, who makes sure his staff of brainiacs gets a healthy breakfast and a personalized dinner for late-night projects (note the food connection again). He offers vacation grants to induce people to rest their brains and reinvigorate their creativity. Charlie says, "It's important to create the conditions that allow others to do the great things they are meant to do." Pretty powerful stuff.

And Charlie puts his money where his mouth is. He *measures* his team's creativity and productivity and has proof that a combination of playing, eating well, and working produces substantially better results than coalmine-style management.

Eric Severson, Gap's executive in charge of talent (who wrote the Foreword to this book), installed a Results Only Work Environment (ROWE) at Gap headquarters. Employees are encouraged to take charge of their whole lives. They are completely responsible to choose when to work, where to work, what meetings to attend, what calls to join, and anything else that impacts their results. The idea is for employees to establish a sustainable personal rhythm that helps them be creative, productive, and yes, happy.

What have the business gains been for Next Jump and Gap? Simply huge.

What we're finally beginning to realize, on a widespread level, is that our happiness *must* inspire our work, and work *must* inspire our happiness. In order for that to happen, though, our work can't just be any old work; it must be our TRUE work.

TRUE work lies at the heart of TRUE happiness.

What do I mean by this?

TRUE Work

Think about superheroes in the movies. They always have one special thing they do extraordinarily well. So do you, whether you know it or not. My experience has taught me that each of us has a unique "superpower" to make a difference that we alone can make. Your superpower is perhaps your most vital source of intrinsic joy. It is at the core of your TRUE work—that's the work you are designed to do, the work that makes *your* signature impact on the world, the work that *matters* most to you.

Your current job may not be your TRUE work. Sometimes, work is just work. Sometimes you just need a paycheck to get to the next stone in the river. But you must not allow paycheck-only jobs to become your life sentence. Your TRUE work is much bigger than that. It is nothing less than the total value you create for yourself and others throughout your life. Some jobs and roles magnify your positive impact. Others constrain it. The best work for you (whether paid or not) is work that spurs you to use your

40

motivated talents, express your purpose, and serve the world. It is work that allows you to unleash your superpower. This is your TRUE work.

Here is what I mean by TRUE work:

T – Talent. TRUE work engages your talents. Work you feel gifted at performing is work you are naturally good at. You may not be great at it right now, but with some pleasant effort, you may indeed go from good to great.

R – Reward. TRUE work is intrinsically rewarding, because it is both meaningful and enjoyable. It is work you love so much you have a hard time stopping.

U – Uniqueness. Your TRUE work is uniquely yours. It allows you to put your unique mark or expression on it. This is what generates passion, whether your work is baking pies, developing computer code, or nursing at-risk babies. When the unique imprint you put on your work makes a crucial difference, it becomes a calling, not just a job.

E – Evolution. Your TRUE work drives you to evolve into the best person you're capable of becoming. It also contributes to the evolution of humanity as a whole. (For a powerful course on how to discover your TRUE work, visit *http://www.thoughtrocket.com/true-happiness* and look for the "Turn Your Superpower Into Your Career" course.) Your greatest contribution to the world comes not so much from *hard* work as it does from *TRUE work*. Your TRUE

41

work is unique to you and can only be discovered *by* you. Your TRUE work uses your superpower at its core. What sidetracks us is getting confused, exhausted, and fearful in reaction to life's difficulties. It becomes easier to slowly lower our expectations than to seek our TRUE work.

Yet no matter how we try to fool ourselves, TRUE work is critical to our happiness.

Work – Life Harmony: The TRUE Recipe for Happiness

TRUE work, in fact, is the key lever for our entire quality of life.

TRUE Work

Work-Life Harmony

TRUE Love   **TRUE Play**

The reason TRUE work is so essential is this: When we are doing our TRUE work, we maximize our impact for the effort we are exerting. Because TRUE work leverages our unique talents in a way that is meaningful and rewarding to us, we create more value in less time. This in turn gives us the time we need to nurture our most rewarding relationships and enjoy a sustainable lifestyle. The meshing of these three elements—TRUE work, TRUE love (relationships), and TRUE play (lifestyle)—is what creates real work - life harmony. And that, my friends, is TRUE happiness.

Understand this: TRUE happiness does not result from trying to achieve *balance*. No. Balance is all about allotting equal time and attention to competing priorities. Trying to achieve work - life *balance* will kill you. It requires soul killing amounts of self-discipline followed by failure. Most often time management and priority juggling *creates* more stress than it relieves. What may not be intuitive is that the launch pad of inner harmony comes from pursuing your TRUE work—work that *strengthens* your life-force rather than weakens it. This kind of work inspires deep and meaningful relationships with your family, friends, and colleagues. It also enables you to *live* a high-quality lifestyle, rather than *buy* one. TRUE work is not a drain on your soul that must be carefully managed; it is *food* for your soul.

The Three Passions of Work - Life Harmony

What creates work - life harmony—TRUE happiness—is an equal *passion* for work, love, and play. When you are intrinsically motivated by all three areas of your life, investing yourself in them doesn't require self-discipline. Instead, a natural harmony results when passions are ignited in all three realms. If we are only passionate in one dimension of our lives, we can quickly get out of harmony. That's because passions exert a gravitational force that can suck up all of our attention.

For instance, when we are performing our TRUE work, we feel a natural passion to give it our all. That's great, of course, but it can overwhelm other parts of our lives. It can push away friends and family and rob time from surfing, gardening, going to concerts, or other playful passions that make our life worth loving.

To enjoy TRUE happiness you must have *three* roughly equal passions—a passion for your work, a passion for your loved ones, and a passion for engaging in a hobby or interest.

Three big passions—that's the key. The force of each passion keeps the others in harmony. If you can't wait to be alone with your life partner or your best friend, *and* you can't imagine NOT making time for your passionate interests—like surfing or playing the piano—then you have all the ingredients of TRUE happiness. When you have three big passions, each one *naturally insists* upon being given time and attention. Time management is not required.

There is really only one true success, and that is the quality of your entire life. There is no joy like the joy of baking your one-of-a-kind superpower into your work, your relationships, *and* your lifestyle, all in beautiful harmony.

TRUE Passions

It turns out that the same four elements that make up your TRUE work also make up the other two "legs" of TRUE happiness, Love and Play.

TRUE Love: When you use your innate *Talents* and abilities to ferociously love your special people, joy explodes in your life. This creates waves of positive energy that *Reward* you intrinsically. TRUE relationships are those in which you are fully accepted, in all your *Unique* messiness. And in which you embrace others the same way. And of course, TRUE relationships are those that motivate you to *Evolve* to a better version of yourself.

TRUE Play: Similarly, TRUE interests are those that develop your *Talents*, are inherently *Rewarding* to you, allow for your *Unique* self-expression, and help you *Evolve* as a more interesting and skillful person.

If you don't yet have the three passions of work - life harmony, make it your life's work to discover them. Open new doors, experiment with new activities, and when you feel the fuel of passion ignite, double down your energies. If you already have the three passions, invest more of yourself in each of them.

Go ahead; make your life as enriching as it can be. TRUE work, TRUE love, and TRUE play are indeed the TRUE recipe for a delicious life.

That is the point of this whole book.

For many of you, TRUE happiness may sound like an impossible dream. Let me assure you that it's not. It's a dream that comes true every day for many, many people. How? By being intentional about how they work, live, and play. And, of course, how they eat. Real people are doing this every day, and reaping the benefits.

TRUE Happiness in Action
I met Howard Benedict when I was surfing my favorite spot near Cardiff-by-the-Sea. He was 62, tan, fit, smiling, and effortlessly gliding on glassy green waves. Howard grew up in a working-class family in Southern California. He was hypnotized by the Pacific at an early age, and immersed himself in skin-diving, fishing, surfing, and sailing. He had no plans for college, but was eventually inspired to work his way through USC dental school. He loved it. You see, Howard had a natural, easy-going love for everyone. And he loved working with his hands. So painless dentistry became his TRUE work.

Ah, but his passion for play led him to a very unusual approach to his profession. In his beachside practice he saw patients from 2 in the afternoon until 9 at night, four days a week, three weeks a month, ten months a year. He designed his work schedule so that he could pursue his TRUE play with gusto. He sailed, skin-dived, fished, and surfed all over the Pacific, from San Diego to Australia.

46

In his mid-thirties he met his TRUE love, Jennifer, who shared his enthusiasm for the sea and daily adventure. Soon their daughter Bridget showed up; she too was swept up in this TRUE-life adventure of sailing and surfing.

Howard passed away a few months ago. He left behind a thousand friends. His TRUE purpose in life was to love everyone. His attitude was that every person he met was "the best person" and every wave was epic. Howard swam in a warm ocean of work - life harmony. He passed with no regrets. Howard didn't break any laws except the law of conformity. He simply lived a life of TRUE happiness because he wove the three passions of work, love, and play into one amazing life.

Of course you don't have to be a surfing dentist to create work - life harmony.

Meet Catrina (Cat). She is super busy leading the team in charge of "talent engagement" at the giant Gap Brand. Her work - life harmony follows the TRUE recipe with an exclamation point! Cat's personal passion for learning and teaching the secrets of human well-being unite the joys of her life. She loves her company and her work, which focuses on promoting health, optimism, creativity, and commitment among employees. She promotes the ideal of Better You, Better Gap. This job did not exist five years ago, but when workplace trends began to value the health and happiness of workers, Cat was prepared.

Cat is also the mother of three, ages 16, 8, and 4, who together with her husband, Terry (who works at Trader Joe's), form a high-energy family with all the joys and challenges that brings. Her vegan diet stimulates weekly family visits to farmer's markets, where she teaches her children nutrition by example. And recently she bought "fitbits" for herself and Terry. Fitbits are devilishly addictive devices that fit on your belt and track the effects of your daily movement from walking to stair climbing. It also tells you how long and how restfully you sleep. Catrina's children pit her against Terry in a daily competition. On Sundays a truce is declared and Cat and Terry go on a 5-mile walk-and-talk. She told me the communication and closeness payoffs of their Sunday walks has poured buckets of positive energy into their marriage of 17 years.

Work, love, and play all united in a joy filled daily rhythm. That's work - life harmony.

That's what my happiness recipes are designed to do for you. They will help you create new habits that will increase your opportunities for TRUE happiness.

Habit is the key to change. And recipes are the key to

changing habits. Is it all becoming clear?

Good. Now there's just one more thing we need to do before diving into the recipes. We need to find a way to make the new habits stick. We need a cooking tool.

X-Change: The Universal Cooking Tool

The key to making real change is every day, sustained effort. Oddly, the secret on how to do this comes from Jerry. Yep, *that* Jerry Seinfeld.

I don't know Jerry personally, but he tells a very useful story about how to change our habits. It seems that at a certain point in his career, Jerry developed a negative tendency—namely, a failure to write new jokes. Headlining comedians typically do shows that are ninety minutes long and require at least sixty really good jokes, sometimes twice that number. And they must constantly add *new* jokes to stay relevant. So it's a never-ending challenge. And it's stressful. In fact, for Jerry it was so stressful that he developed a procrastination habit as big as a fire-breathing dragon. However, the negative payoff from avoiding writing was career suicide, so he needed to change.

Here's what I read he did. He asked himself, "If I can't write a hundred great new jokes, what can I do?" The answer was to write *one*. One good new joke a day. On average, it would take him twenty minutes to write one good joke. Twenty minutes a day to save his career? Even Jerry could do that!

To support himself in this, he created a simple tracking tool that brain science confirms is very clever. It is based on our emotional revulsion to observing our own failure. It worked like this. Jerry got some large, blank monthly calendars and put them on his bathroom wall. Every day that he successfully wrote a good joke, he would put a big red "X" across that day. Before long, a pattern formed and then he absolutely, positively did not want to break the chain of red X's. (Sitting and staring at a calendar of success or failure a few times every day seems to really motivate us to do whatever it takes to earn that red X.)

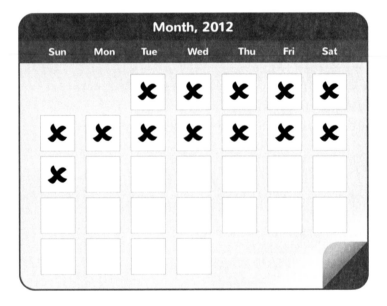

You see, our brains respond emotionally to visual cues. Visuals give us a quick, powerful way of confirming that we are keeping our commitments, that we are staying true to our deepest values, that we are in the driver's seat. We like these visual emotional messages. And they actually trigger a small release of the pleasure chemical dopamine every time we view them.

I call this process X-Change, as in give yourself a big red *X* for every day you keep your commitment to *change* your habit.

Here's how to do it. Choose one of the 8 habits of daily happiness you'll read about in the next part of the book. Print the PDF of the monthly calendar (see my website at *http://www.thoughtrocket.com/true-happiness*). Tape it up on a wall you see several times a day, and start marking an X on each day you keep your promise to do the habit. See how many days you can link together in a "chain of change." As you begin to succeed, add more habits. Just print an additional X-Change calendar sheet for each habit and tape it next to your first X-Change calendar. Yeah, go ahead and wallpaper your bathroom with them. Seeing your daily progress makes success easier, because success breeds success.

I'll let you in on a secret that sports psychologist Alan Fine taught me. If you actually do this daily—that is, mark an X when you do it, leave it blank if you fail—you *will* succeed in engraining a new happiness habit. But beware of an interesting phenomenon. If you *don't* do your new habit but you *do* keep track, you'll start to see more and more blank spots beneath the dates, and your impulse will be to tear down the calendar. The reason? We don't like to track our own failure. We will either track our daily success with a big fat X *or* we will rip down the chart because we can't stand to be visually reminded of failing. So just commit to *tracking* your success or failure for thirty full days, and you *will* succeed. It's the *tracking* that connects you to the commitment. Pretty cool.

Of course we often link this process of habit change with changing bad habits or doing healthy things we don't initially enjoy. Yet I have spent my life working with high achievers who are experts at self-denial. As their thinking goes, doing something that might be personally fulfilling must be avoided because there is work to be done and duties to attend to. This bad habit is so strong in many that they can't tell me what they enjoy anymore. So I ask them keep an x-change calendar to track their new habit of playing or "wasting" time with a friend or loved one. Self-denial can be a useful strength unless you are denying your TRUE self.

Let's Get Started

Okay, now it's time to look at the two kinds of recipes you will need to change your life. Again, some of these are food recipes and some are behavior recipes. These recipes will help you wisely invest your time, energy, and talent while steering your life toward TRUE happiness. To make things simple, I have organized the recipes around a typical workday. (I've also included variations for stay-at-home caregivers.)

Ready to give it a go? To embark on this adventure of

change, you just need to do three things:

1) Eat like a happy person. Be smart about the food you eat and keep your vitality high. Use my recipes, and find or create some of your own.
2) Try whichever happiness recipes appeal to you and track them using the X-Change tracker.
3) Tell us what's happening. Why? Social support drives positive change. We urge you to link up with others who are interested in the same things you are. We urge you to seek encouragement from fellow climbers who have already been to the top of the mountain you are climbing. And we urge you to ask us questions, so that we can help you in whatever ways we can. To connect with others who are doing what you're doing, just click here: *http://www.thoughtrocket.com/true-happiness*.

Are you hungry for change? Great, then let's dig into some recipes.

Part 2: The Recipes

Symbol Key

 This icon represents a Happiness Recipe. I've provided recipes you can use from the moment you awaken until your head hits the pillow at night. Each one is short and combined with an action habit.

 This icon represents a Food or Beverage Recipe. I've included recipes for delicious, healthy snacks and meals, from the super simple to the more complex, that can carry you all the way through your day.

 This icon represents an X-Change action habit, something specific you can do and track every day. Give yourself a big red *X* for every day you keep your commitment to *change* your habit.

Your Daily Happiness Recipe Schedule

 Happiness Recipe 1: Good Morning Harmony

 Happiness Recipe 2: The Habit of Super Flow

 Happiness Recipe 3: Stretch Yourself

 Happiness Recipe 4: Learn What You Love

 Happiness Recipe 5: Half-Time: Recovery, Refreshment, Social Connection

Happiness Recipe 6: Life Is a Gym

 Happiness Recipe 7: Silent Night, Loving Night

 Happiness Recipe 8: Unplug, Rest, Recharge

Happiness Recipe 1: Good Morning Harmony

I like to shower in the morning. The warm water soothes my back and wakes me in a way that is firm and gentle. Well, how about a morning shower for your mind?

Instead of lurching awake with an urgency that ignites stress and overwhelm, why not use your first moments of wakefulness to refresh your sense of purpose and exert a firm and gentle control over your day? This is a great way to set the stage for TRUE happiness on a daily basis.

Here's how.

 HAPPINESS RECIPE 1: Good Morning Harmony

Your Trigger
Waking up. Make it your daily cue to Zen your way into your day.

Your Response

1. Lying flat on your back, still under your sheets, with your arms relaxed at your side, take three slow, deep breaths. Deep breathing tells your brain everything is calm. That's right. The simple act of deep breathing calms your mind-body down. That's because when we are threatened, we breathe rapid, shallow breaths, and this signals our mind-body to tense up. This gets your panic on.

   Deep, slow breathing does the opposite. It sends oxygen to your brain so you can think faster and more clearly, which also calms your nervous system. So begin with three deep, slow breaths. Inhale through your nose and exhale through your mouth to expel all CO_2 possible. You don't want global warming of the brain. Too much CO_2 slows down your synapses, dulling your thinking and feeling. Three deep breaths, okay?

2. Next, think of something you are really grateful for. It should be an original thought each morning. On your first days, you may think of things like your family or your health, but soon you'll move on to things like indoor plumbing. Just recently I recognized I was grateful for: comfortable shoes, my children's good jobs, the last movie I saw, the view from my office, and my wife's special oatmeal. If you make the smallest effort, you'll notice a torrent of things to appreciate. It is very soothing, uplifting, and surprising.

Now settle your mind on the single new thing you want to feel gratitude for this morning. Put 100% of your attention on it. One way to increase the feeling of gratitude is to imagine your life without it. The point is, *feel* the gratitude, don't just think it. *Feel* well-being. Feeling is different from conceptual thinking. That's an analytical act. It does little to ignite the happiness explosion waiting to erupt in your mind-body. *Feeling* gratitude is what does that.

Go ahead and keep breathing as you feel a golden glow of gratitude flood over you.

The Magic of Gratitude

Even if we're masters at creating happiness, it's not a permanent condition. That's why Dr. Martin Seligman, the founder of Positive Psychology, found the best question to ask is not "*Am* I happy?" but rather "*How often* do I feel happy?" Feelings of well-being actually *increase in frequency* when we become more aware of them. This sense of "Wow, life is great right this minute" accelerates the production of mood-lifting brain chemicals, deepens our bonds with others, and increases our capacity to feel positive.

Recently, social scientists have been using texting to track people's happiness. They text-message volunteers at random intervals, seven times a day, and ask them to rate their level of happiness at the moment the text arrives.

The surprising discovery the researchers have made is that *just asking people* if they are happy makes most people feel more happiness. Most subjects report feeling good more often as they participate in the study day after day.

Why? The main ingredient in happiness seems to be gratitude. People who are *aware* of the good things in their lives are happier than people who take good things for granted.

Just noticing happiness seems to motivate us to look for things that are good in life, and to feel grateful for them. It's like turning a bank of floodlights on parts of our lives that were hidden in darkness. And in doing so, we spontaneously feel happier.

3. Now, ask yourself the Big Three Questions:

   First, what's the most important thing I can do today for someone I love? Let the answer come. It might be to make a call, write a love note, or do someone a favor. Just think of one thing you might do that demonstrates sincere caring and support for a loved one. Keep the idea of TRUE love in mind.

   Second, what's the most important thing I can do today for my TRUE work? *TRUE* work is the big idea here. Your present job may not be your TRUE work. Its urgencies keep you focused on putting out today's fires. Your TRUE work—your career, your calling, your bigger contribution—beckons you forward. Get clear and re-commit to your best future. Consider the question: If I could do one thing today to invest in my TRUE work, what would it be? Today's job is only a step on your career path. You need to be accelerating your whole *career*, no matter what your current job urgencies are. Figure out the one thing that would make the biggest difference to your TRUE work today and do that.

Third, what's the most import thing I can do today for my TRUE lifestyle? This question might spur a commitment to improve some aspect of your diet, exercise, or sleep. It may be to de-clutter your home, plant some flowers or make time to play at something you love doing—TRUE play.

Finally, ask yourself, "Is there anything else I can do today to improve my TRUE happiness? It might be planning a date, a vacation, or a great dinner. It might involve taking a step toward improving your finances. Early in the morning, your subconscious mind, which has been processing thoughts all night, often has important ideas to inspire your conscious mind. The point is to do something specific to grow your three passions. Whatever comes up, take note of it. Do it.

4. And speaking of taking notes, here's the most important part of this first habit. Keep a journal at

your bedside. It doesn't have to be fancy. A small spiral notebook works fine. As you take a final deep breath, rise and reach for your journal and write down the three most important things you've chosen to do that day. Just write them as short bullet points. Writing is important because it helps your brain remember.

If you do this habit the moment you awaken, the entire "Good Morning Harmony" ritual takes only about five minutes—the breathing, the gratitude moment, and the three most important things. That's because your mind is not yet cluttered with a dumpster of urgencies. You're not yet confused or distracted. You get instant answers to simple questions. You are able to tap into your brain's overnight prioritizing work.

Payoff

Imagine what your life might feel like thirty days from now if you spent thirty days doing the three most important things, no matter what other daily urgencies required your attention. It feels pretty *bleep*ing good. Because you've opened an investment account in your best future. By doing the three most important things, you are making valuable deposits in yourself, your relationships, and your career. People who do this for ninety days report a much greater sense of control over their lives, as well as more optimism and clarity. Most of all, they say they are happier.

Carry "Good Morning Harmony" Into Your Day

To build on and reinforce Good Morning Harmony, use the beginning, middle, and end of your workday to re-prioritize your three most important things. Famed researcher Daniel Pink told me that personal autonomy over what work we do and when we do it are super-drivers of personal motivation. So try this:

- As you begin work, spend the first 15-30 minutes taking charge of your inbox and your schedule. The solution to stress isn't an empty inbox. It's an inbox *you've filled yourself.* It's up to you to fill your inbox with things you truly care about. Eliminate whatever activities aren't critical to the one thing you can do today. What meetings can you not attend? What conference calls can you get the notes on later? How can you do an end run around time-wasting activities?

- At 11:45 a.m., stop what you're doing and spend fifteen minutes talking to someone you deeply care about: a parent, a child, a friend, your spouse. Express your gratitude for them, tell them what they mean to you, share a recent experience you had, or ask how you can help them achieve one of *their* important goals.

- Spend the last thirty minutes of your workday actively disengaging. Work, just like a work*out*, requires a cool-down afterward. Stop answering emails and phone calls, mindfully clean up your workspace, and slow your pace down to create a growing sense of calm. Think about the one thing you can do for your TRUE play (lifestyle). Before

you get up to leave, count to 30 as you gently
breathe in and out.

 X-Change

Changing everything at once can be stressful. Since there
are eight happiness habits in this book, doing them all
might seem daunting. Yet big change can be easier to
sustain than small change, because it's big change that
produces tangible results in 21 days (the length of time it
takes a new habit to form). It's usually better to start
regular exercise, hire a trainer, take yoga, and improve
your diet all at once, than to just give up candy. Why?
Because in three weeks you'll feel different, and it's
progressive improvement that motivates continued
change. So thoughtfully choose two or three of these
happiness recipes, and do them every day for 21 days.
Choose ones you most naturally want to do. Remember,
with each habit, download my free calendar template, and
mark a big red X through every day you complete your
habit. Make a string of 7 X's to see how this habit works for
you. And if you decide to make it permanent, keep that
string of X's going!

If Good Morning Harmony is a recipe that rings your bell,
put an X through every day you do the morning exercise
and complete at least one of the "one things" you wrote
down. Later, you can require the completion of two, then
all three, of your daily "one things" in order to earn an X.

My research team has created a website and a social community to help you make your new habits permanent. It's called ThoughtRocket.com. We want you to tell the Thought Rocket community what's working for you! Encourage, inspire, and ask questions. You can make a difference. Your words may inspire another to take action. So come join us at *http://www.thoughtrocket.com/true-happiness*.

Special Habit for Moms or Dads Who Are Domestic Engineers

It can be hard to take even a few minutes for Good Morning Harmony if your baby is crying, or your kids are jumping on your bed at 5 in the morning. But you can still incorporate the essentials of this habit, even when you have to hit the ground running.

If your kids are old enough to follow directions, get them in on the action. Start with the deep inhale and deep exhale. Keep them engaged by making it a little more kinetic, stretching their arms open wide while inhaling and then dropping their arms at their sides with each exhale. Next, do some slow shoulder rolls, then rotate one wrist and then the other, one ankle and then the other, all while each person says something they are grateful for. Even if they say something silly, just roll with it.

65

They'll catch on eventually.

If you're dealing with infants and toddlers, take it slow. As long as they know you're holding them or guiding them, you can go as slow as you want to. Take your deep breaths as you lead them, and moderate your movement to be slow and deliberate. Let your body and mind wake up slowly. And recite your gratitude to yourself as you go.

A Few Nutrition Principles

As we get into the food recipes, let's take a quick look at some wise nutrition principles. These come from chef/nutritionist Florence Quinn (*http://www.aboutfood.biz*) and Heather Fleming, CCN, whose website, *http://www.consciousnutrition.com*, is also a great resource for healthy, creative eating. I've also merged in the wisdom of Dr. Oz, and obesity researcher Judith Stein, SCDRD, who teaches at the University of California, Davis.

I especially like professor Stein's relationship with food. She says, "Chocolate should be an honorary vitamin." This is from an expert who's published over 250 papers, so she ought to know.

Here are their principles that I try to follow:
- Never be really full or really hungry.
- Eat foods or combinations of food that don't break

down quickly into simple sugars. (Avoid corn syrup or foods with sugar in the first five ingredients.)

- Eat complex carbohydrates, 100% whole grains, etc.
- Eat lots of fiber and lots of protein in the morning—this will decrease your appetite and give you more energy throughout the day.
- Having a bit of protein every time you eat will nearly always make you feel full longer.
- Choose organic, free range, or grass-fed whenever possible.
- Eat local and seasonal; visit your farmers' market regularly instead of relying exclusively on supermarkets.
- Eat good fat from nuts and olives, as well as olive oil or fish oils
- Always eat 100% whole foods. If you drink milk, drink at least 1% or 2% and use real butter, just sparingly. (Your body knows how to use nature's ingredients to make you healthy.)
- Eat loads of raw or lightly cooked vegetables.
- Substitute almond milk for the dairy kind if you like.
- Avoid foods that don't taste good to you.
- Try the 80% diet. It's the best diet I was ever given. Just trim 20% off the amount you currently eat, and you'll be amazed how much weight you'll lose.

Breakfast Recipes

READY FOR BREAKFAST?

Now that you are wide awake and have done Good Morning Harmony, you are ready for breakfast. Of course, if you want to do some vigorous morning exercise, do that first, after a 50-to-100-calorie healthy snack and at least 8 ounces of water. But whatever your morning rituals and responsibilities are, eat a real breakfast before you start work.

Make sure to rehydrate your body to revive your muscles and boost your immune system. Next, visualize the healthiest version of you. Take 60 seconds to see your body at your ideal fitness weight. See yourself with high vitality. See yourself making healthy food and lifestyle choices throughout the day and evening. Feel free to ask for strength from your spiritual "source," whatever that might be. Great - now it's time to eat.

Athlete's Oatmeal

> ⅓ cup Coach's Oats (developed by Lynn Rogers, champion gymnastics coach)
> ⅛ cup almond milk
> ¼ tsp. ground cinnamon
> ¼ tsp. almond or vanilla extract
> ¼ cup sliced almonds, roasted

¼ cup diced apples, pears, or berries

Bring water to a rapid boil. Add Coach's Oats.

Reduce heat to medium and cook for 5 minutes, stirring occasionally. Remove from heat, cover, and let stand for 1 minute.

Mix in almond milk, then add almond or vanilla extract. Add fruit on top with sliced almonds. Chow down.

I always eat this before I give a three-hour morning speech. It tastes great and keeps me going.

Heather's Breakfast Enchiladas

<u>Ingredients for Enchiladas & Filling</u>
8 corn tortillas
2 cups chopped zucchini or summer squash (or combo of the two)
1 onion, chopped
1-2 cloves garlic, minced

<u>Ingredients for Sauce</u>
1 onion, chopped
1 garlic clove, minced
2 cups water
½ can diced tomatoes (14.5 oz. can)
1 lb. green chili (frozen, chopped)

<u>Make Sauce</u>
Sauté chopped onion on low heat for 10 minutes.
Do not over-brown, but cook slowly.

Add garlic, cook for 30 seconds.
Add water, diced tomatoes, and green chili.
Simmer for 30 minutes.

<u>Make Filling</u>
Sauté zucchini, summer squash, or combination,
with onion and garlic, until tender but not
overcooked, about 5-6 minutes.

Warm corn tortillas in microwave for 30 seconds.
Fill each with 1/8 of the filling, fold and place, seam
down, in 9 X 13 pan. Pour sauce over them. Cover
and bake at 375° for 25-35 minutes. When bubbly,
remove from oven.

*Most people today seem to love onion and garlic. But
if you want to reduce the quantity in these recipes,
feel free. Personally, I think onion and garlic are
overdone. A little kicky flavor is great, but our
current fad with over-spicing food leads to a garlic
fog around our bodies that doesn't smell so great to
others... just saying.*

Florence's Banana Nut Oatmeal Muffins (dairy free)

*These muffins smell so good when they come out
of the oven. The ripe bananas give them a lot of*

natural sweetness, and therefore the recipe contains very little added sugar. The coconut oil and the addition of oatmeal give them that nutty goodness.

(Makes 12 medium size muffins)

<u>Dry Mix</u>
1 cup (150 g) all-purpose flour
1 cup (135g) whole wheat, rye or graham flour
1 ½ tsp. baking powder
½ tsp. baking soda
½ tsp. salt
1 tsp. ground cinnamon

<u>Wet Mix</u>
1/3 cup (85 g) coconut oil (or unsalted butter if you prefer)
¼ cup (50 g) natural brown cane sugar
1 large egg
3 large (560 g) mashed ripe bananas
2 Tbsp. molasses or agave nectar
½ cup (80 g) cooked oatmeal, preferably from steel cut oats
¾ cup (100 g) pecans or walnuts, roughly chopped

<u>Dry Mix</u>
Place both flours, baking powder and baking soda, salt and cinnamon in a bowl. Set aside.

<u>Wet Mix</u>

Whisk coconut oil and sugar until creamy. Add egg, mashed bananas, molasses or agave nectar, cooked oatmeal and nuts and mix in.

Fold the wet mix into the dry mix and stir until just combined.

Lightly oil muffin pan with coconut oil. Spoon the batter into the pan. Bake in a preheated oven at 350° for 30-40 minutes, or until golden brown and tester comes out clean. Set aside to cool.

The muffins are best eaten within eight hours, but will keep for a couple days. The uncooked batter can be kept in the refrigerator for five days. So you can bake them as you need them and have freshly baked muffins every morning... nice.

Will's Easy Breakfast: Organic Eggs in a Nest

2 slices of sprouted grain bread
1 Tbsp. unsalted butter
2 large eggs
Pinch of coarse sea salt
Ground black pepper to taste

Spread the bread—both sides—with about half of the butter. Put the rest of the butter into a large skillet and melt it over medium heat.

Use a round cookie or biscuit cutter, or the open

rim of a drinking glass, to cut a hole in each slice of buttered bread.

Place the bread slices on the skillet, side by side. Crack two eggs (one at a time) and carefully pour them into the two holes in the bread. When the eggs begin to firm up, flip the bread/egg slices over and cook until they are as soft or firm as you like them. Make sure you grill and eat the round bread "holes" as well.

These are great. Your kids will love them. So will your inner kid.

Debbie and Heather's Healthy French Toast

    1 orange
    2 slices sprouted grain bread
    2 eggs
    ⅛ cup almond milk or whole milk
    Cinnamon
    Organic vanilla extract
    Coconut oil for cooking

Mix eggs, milk, cinnamon, and vanilla extract in a bowl. Squeeze all the juice from the orange into mixture. Grate ⅓ of the orange peel and add to mix. Dip the bread until thoroughly wet. Heat skillet with one teaspoon of coconut oil. Place the bread in the skillet and cook on medium heat until golden brown on each side. Top with organic butter, ghee, or almond butter and organic maple syrup.

Okay, I used to make French toast with white bread and eggs and drown them in maple-flavored corn syrup. What a waste of calories. The cinnamon, vanilla and oranges are the magic here. Also, you can substitute French brioche for the sprouted grain bread, if you are willing to have just one piece— eyow! Also, only use real maple syrup from Vermont or Canada. Yes, it's more expensive than high-fructose poison, but you're worth it.

Heather's Healthy Pancakes
(In honor of Jack Johnson's "Banana Pancake" song)

I love listening to Jack Johnson songs on the weekend. He is a surfer, and has a surfer's viewpoint on enjoying life. His music sounds like he feels. He has a song about Banana Pancakes. Here's how to make them:

2 cups brown rice flour
½ tsp. baking soda
1 tsp. sea salt
1 tsp. cinnamon
20 drops vanilla crème stevia
3 eggs (preferably free-range)
1 ripe banana
1 ¾ cups rice or almond milk (for more richness add coconut milk)

Coconut oil for cooking

Heat coconut oil in skillet at low-medium setting.

In a bowl, mix wet ingredients together with mashed banana.

Add dry ingredients, mixing well.

Pour desired amount of batter (more for bigger pancakes, less for smaller) into hot pan. Cook for about 3 minutes or until you can easily slide a spatula under the pancake to flip it over. Cook another 2 to 3 minutes. Repeat for remaining batter.

Try topping with almond butter, ghee, maple syrup, honey, and/or fresh fruit. Makes about 7 large, hearty pancakes. Very filling. Serves 6-7. Enjoy!

WEEKEND BREAKFAST

Heather's Vegetable Frittata
8 large organic free-range eggs
¾ cup organic milk (optional)
½ tsp. sea salt
¼ tsp. freshly ground pepper
3 Tbsp. grapeseed oil
1 medium onion, thinly sliced
1 all-purpose potato (around 7 ounces), cut into 3/8-inch cubes

1 cup small broccoli florets
1 cup small cauliflower florets
2 cups spinach
5 Tbsp. fresh goat cheese

Preheat oven to 375°. Beat eggs, milk, salt, and pepper in medium bowl.
Heat oil over medium heat in nonstick (10-inch) sauté pan. Add onions and potatoes and cook until potatoes are softened, about 8 minutes, stirring occasionally.

Stir in broccoli, spinach, and cauliflower. Cook until vegetables are tender, about 10 minutes, stirring occasionally.

Reduce heat to low and pour in egg mixture. Drop small spoonfuls of goat cheese on top. Cook about 2 more minutes on the stovetop.

Transfer to oven and bake 20 to 25 minutes, or until the top is golden brown and the eggs have just set in the center. (Note: if you are using a skillet with a nonmetal handle, wrap it with double-thick aluminum foil before placing in oven.)

Remove from oven and slide cooked frittata out of pan onto a cutting board. Cut into wedges and serve warm.

This takes time, but mindful preparation with a partner makes it extra delicious.

SWEET AND SAVORY SMOOGIES

My son, Fun Boy, and his wife live in a small town in the Northwest. The local city dump serves great smoothies. I know it sounds crazy, but when you take your trash to the dump, you pay on the way out and there's a little pay station that sells smoothies. Anyway, my little three-year-old granddaughter will clamor to go to the city dump every Saturday so she can get a "smoogie!"

Smoogies are a fast way to get lots of nutrients, but be careful of the dense calories. A 12-ounce protein smoogie is a full meal, not a snack. (It's easy to get a smoogie-belly thinking you're on a healthy diet. Even too much of a good thing is too much.)

Berry Coconut Smoogie

1 cup mixed organic berries
2 scoops of whey-based protein powder
1 cup coconut milk
2 tsp. unsweetened cocoa powder
1 tsp. honey

Combine ingredients in a blender. Blend on high until well mixed. Pour in a glass.

Chocolate Almond Smoogie

3 tsp. almond butter
¼ cup coconut milk

2 tsp. cocoa powder
½-1 cup ice
2-4 Tbsp. water (or other liquid)
Combine ingredients in a blender. Blend on high
until well mixed. Pour in a glass.

Spicy Tomato Smoogie

½ cup chopped tomato
¼ cup chopped cucumber
½ ripe avocado
1/3 cup frozen spinach, or small handful raw
spinach
1 tsp. hot sauce or black pepper, or to taste
Squeeze of lemon
½ cup ice

Combine ingredients in a blender. Blend on high
until well mixed. Pour in a glass.

Vanilla Berry Smoogie

⅓ cup organic frozen berries
¼ cup coconut water

Combine ingredients in a blender. Blend on high
until well mixed. Pour in a glass.

Pumpkin Smoogie Dessert

¼ cup pumpkin puree

1 banana, fresh or frozen
½ cup coconut milk
Dash of cinnamon
1 teaspoon honey

Combine ingredients in a blender. Blend on high until well mixed. Pour in a glass. Garnish with a sprinkle of cinnamon. Enjoy!

Okay, this is like Thanksgiving dessert. If you like pumpkin pie, you'll love this. Eight ounces is plenty. Taste the tastiness!

Drew's Recipes

Drew, who lives in Montreal, is a serious foodie. He takes his wife and kids on these find-the-best-of- fresh- food missions, and then comes home and involves everyone in meal preparation.

Cooking is a dance Drew performs. No, he's not some art guy; he develops computer code for artificial intelligence. He just loves food. So I asked for some recipes, and he gave me these crazy, elaborate, sensational creations. I include them with a warning. Of course they taste amazing, but he includes a few ingredients that are seemingly unique to Montreal. So you and I will have to find substitutes where we live. Shouldn't be too hard. Also, you'll have to excuse his enthusiastic prose. I must say his food is sublime.

Gourmet Granola

8 ounces Euphoria Gourmet Granola

1 ½ Tbsp. freshly ground peanut butter
¼ cup raw walnuts
¼ cup raw pecans
1 Tbsp. 2012 Quebec maple syrup (*extra clair*)
Organic milk as desired
(Serves 1)

From Drew: "I begin with a bowl filled with Euphoria Gourmet Granola made in Montreal by La Fourmi Bionique. This granola, made from organic ingredients when available, contains, in addition to the standard list, hunks of high-quality milk chocolate and ground marshmallow root. The granola itself has been baked to a wonderful golden brown, caramelizing the honey and sugar without drying the oats, spelt, and other grains.

"I add to this several spoonfuls of freshly ground peanut butter from a local nut and coffee bean shop. I add the requisite amount of organic milk to incorporate the ingredients, striving to coat as much of the surface area of the granola as possible. I then add a handful of raw walnuts and pecans from the same nut merchant and drizzle over the top a generous amount of this spring's harvest of Southern Quebec maple syrup, the extra clair variety. These are incorporated again into the whole. The taste and texture make this breakfast special."

Well, I told you he was a foodie.

Happiness Recipe 2: The Habit of Super Flow

Never in history have humans had to process, sort, prioritize, and respond to so many demands, so fast, from so many people. Most of our days are jammed with endless calls for our attention and response. It's an all-out assault. The fact that we've gotten used to being assaulted doesn't make it any less emotionally violent.

Yet happiness is characterized by feelings of optimism, gratefulness, and contentment. And those feelings don't spring from being drowned in deadlines, stress, and overwhelm.

The opposite of overwhelm is mindful presence.

Have you ever been so in love that you felt totally immersed in your loved one's presence? Have you ever been alone in a spectacularly beautiful place and felt completely absorbed by the beauty of the moment?

Those are moments of mindful presence.

If there is one master tool to experiencing TRUE happiness, it is to be mindfully present as often as possible. Usually, we are not. Usually, we are preoccupied by a never-ending stream of other people's urgencies. Or we are beating ourselves up over our regrets about the past, or our fears about an uncertain future. It is only in the natural state of mindfulness that we experience deep life satisfaction and contentment. Mindfulness is a necessary condition to feeling happy.

You see, when our attention is fully in the present, there is no *room* for anxiety.

Becoming mindful is easy and extremely pleasant. It simply means "experiencing your experience." All it requires is a conscious shift in perspective.

Imagine you—the core, authentic you—as the bed of a river. And imagine that in your core bedrock, you have deep, fearless awareness of all your genuine feelings and desires. Now imagine the rushing, roaring torrent of the river as your everyday experience. It's not *you*. It's everything going on outside of you. What happens if you mistake the frantic things happening in the river rapids for *you*? You'll have a hard time not becoming stressed-out, controlling, worried, and unhappy.

But the river is not you. You are the bedrock. And you can access that still bedrock by becoming fully present. That just means to relax, move your attention to the present moment, and calmly shift your perspective away from the choppy waters.

Being fully present is restful and relaxing. It produces vitality for living and loving. It expands your attention. It empowers you to see, hear, and feel things that typically go unnoticed.

Mindful presence is a form of active meditation. It's meditation without withdrawing, chanting, or sitting cross-legged. No, it isn't weird. It is extremely natural, easy, and restful. Oddly, it is also the rarest of all human habits. But if you truly desire to be happy, every recipe starts with mindful presence.

A very closely related term is *flow*. The term was first coined by Mihály Csíkszentmihályi, who found that talented athletes, dancers, and painters frequently get in the performance "zone." Time seems to stop for them, and their abilities are magnified in a totally focused, joyful performance. He found that this "flow state" was available to anyone doing daily tasks they find deeply engaging and intrinsically enjoyable. When we're in flow, work becomes effortless. It still requires energy, but it's joyful effort instead of difficult slogging.

You can put yourself in an endless, connected chain of flow states by doing everything with mindful presence. So preparing a presentation can be done in flow. Helping your daughter with her homework is an opportunity for flow. Coaching a colleague, researching an opportunity, solving a thorny problem—all flow possibilities. Yes, even eating lunch and cleaning toilets can be flow times.

This is, in fact, what Super Flow is all about. It is the art of stringing together the key activities of your day in a series of concentrated, focused sessions of mindful presence to achieve an outcome that *you* decide is meaningful. And nearly any act can *become* meaningful if you approach it according to a certain recipe.

Flow amplifies your attention, your talent, and your ability to improve as you go along. You can reach the state of flow by employing these three conditions:

1. **Establish a clear goal for each activity.** For instance, even your morning send-off of your spouse or partner can have a clear intention. The goal might be sixty seconds of concentrated presence in which you genuinely express love and appreciation for each other. That can create a hot moment of love flow. Likewise, your 9 a.m. meeting with your work team should have a clear goal. The main idea is to apply a *conscious intention* to every activity.

2. **Establish a time frame for the activity.** You'll notice most great athletes play harder in the fourth quarter. Likewise, students study their guts out during finals. Time limitations concentrate your focus and energy.

3. **Finally,** *give mindful presence* **to what is happening as you perform.** Open your mind and sharpen your senses. Listen to others intently.

Look at data with an eye toward questioning assumptions. Ask yourself, "What if the opposite was also true?" An open, attentive mind will speed up both learning and creativity in real time. It will allow you to instantly change your communication style, if you notice you're not getting through. It will make you smarter, wiser, more mentally agile and emotionally intelligent.

These three elements—a clear goal, a finite timeframe, and 100% mindful attention to what's happening—are the key to producing flow. You can create these three conditions throughout your entire day if you choose to. When you do, your life will change. You will accomplish more with less effort, you will connect with people in more meaningful ways, and your sense of well-being will be over the moon.

Here is an example of a "flow day."

You start the day with Habit One: Good Morning Harmony. That's a flow activity. Then you prepare breakfast. That's also a flow opportunity—choosing your food with an intention of fully enjoying it and giving yourself great energy for your day. Next, you are fully present for the eating, relishing the tastes and textures. Then you mindfully say goodbye to your loved ones. If you do it with full presence and a genuine intention of expressing love, guess what? Another moment of pure flow.

Now you commute to work, *really listening* to your favorite music playlist or an audio book—that's flow, too. At work, you spend 15-30 minutes emptying your inbox, totally focusing on what's important and trashing the rest. You take a ten-minute latte break and talk, with full presence, to a colleague about an upcoming project. If you are consciously aware that in such moments of interaction you are building trust and rapport, that's flow, too.

Now you conduct your first meeting. You present an agenda and announce clear meeting objectives. You establish a time boundary of forty-five minutes. You make sure everyone attending really needs to be there. You engage everyone thoughtfully in the vital issues. You come to a conclusion and establish action steps. Congratulations. You've just held a meeting in a group flow state.

If this sounds hard, exhausting, or even crazy, let me assure you it isn't. Super Flow is just a habit. Anyone interested in being happy and productive can quickly master the three conditions for flow and employ them at will.

So why don't we all do this? Well, the world is set up to disrupt our flow. This is the constant assault I was talking about. Here are some assault weapons that destroy our flow on a daily basis:

- **Multi-tasking:** Actually, there is no such thing. For years, the U.S. military has tried using video games to teach soldiers to concentrate on two things at once, but has never succeeded. Concentrating on *one thing at a time* is a better approach. It shortens the total time required to do many tasks, and dramatically reduces errors. Multi-tasking just makes us stupid. Yet our brains fool us by telling us otherwise. Research reveals that the human brain deals with the stress of multi-tasking by squirting out small amounts of dopamine, which chemically induce a false sense of confidence. That's why we think we can text and drive. We can't. Multi-tasking is a killer of flow.

- **Anxiety:** *Worry* also kills flow. However, when we bring our full attention to the present moment, worry evaporates.

- **Boredom:** If you've ever sat through a boring meeting or a boring movie—or how about a boring date?—you know that boredom is a major drain for flow. The antidote for boredom is meaning. Make what you're doing meaningful in some way, and then focus on the meaningful part. Next time you're in a boring meeting, for example, make it your goal to connect with others. Make sure everyone is heard and a real decision is made. This means switching your inner focus off *your* agenda and putting it on the team's purpose. See what happens.

- **Fatigue:** Fatigue also makes us stupid and incapable of concentration. When we're tired, we tend to underperform and behave irritably toward others. So if you are tired, get some rest and reschedule.

- **Distraction and Interruptions:** Many of us live in a raging torrent of emails that we try to respond to in real time. If you do this, research says you will enjoy no more than ten minutes of uninterrupted time in any given day. You cannot do amazing things if you are constantly responding to others' urgencies. Unless you're a 911 operator, you don't need to respond instantly to anyone. Set some time aside, once or twice a day, for responding to emails. And then do *that* with focused intention.

- **Hunger:** That's why this is a recipe book. Low blood sugar slows our brain, interferes with concentration, and dampens creativity. If you are hungry, eat something healthy.

That's a lot of weaponry aimed at disrupting our happiness. Yet Super Flow is the game changer that lets happiness win every time. Here's how to make it *your* habit.

 HAPPINESS RECIPE 2: Super Flow

Trigger
Feeling overwhelmed and frustrated. Feeling that life and work is drudgery. Feeling that you need to escape. Or... Feeling that you want to excel, or soak in the enjoyment of a great experience.

Response
1. Begin each day with Good Morning Harmony. Commit to your three most important things.
2. Stay well fed and watered throughout the day.

3. Plan your times of flow by setting up concentrated sessions of thirty to forty-five minutes of performance, using the three conditions (clear, meaningful goal; fixed time boundaries; 100% mindfulness).
4. After forty-five minutes, take a five- to ten-minute break to refresh yourself and reload your powers of concentration. Listen to some music. Call a friend. Go for a quick walk. Stretch.
5. Keep control of your agenda. Don't randomly respond to incoming emails. Work on work that's meaningful to you, or *make* it so.

If your day gets out of control, restart with step number 3 whenever you're feeling frustrated or overwhelmed. Then continue to make the *rest* of your day an exercise in Super Flow.

Payoff
A feeling of life and work satisfaction. Knowing the strength of your own capabilities. Growing confidence.

 X-Change

For Super Flow, I suggest starting the first week by focusing on one activity each day in which you truly experience flow. Do that and earn your X. The second week, add a second activity, so that you are Super Flowing twice each day for your X. Week three, intentionally do three flow activities. In 21 days, you will be really into Super Flow and will be operating out of your bright inner core much more often.

This habit has a huge payoff. Making even one decision in a state of Super Flow can remake your future, or create success from a tangle of failure. So please give it an earnest try. Then join us on the ThoughtRocket community and tell us what's working or where you are stuck. Go ahead. Ask us your toughest questions (*http://www.thoughtrocket.com/true-happiness*).

Special Habits for Moms or Dads Who Are Domestic Engineers

Set yourself one clear objective to accomplish today, and one second-priority objective (in case the first one gets done way faster than you expected). Work toward this in 30- to 45-minute increments, with five-to-ten-minute breaks. Give yourself a small, healthy snack reward once or twice each morning and afternoon, along with a nice stretch (see Happiness Recipe 3).

Two hazards to avoid:
1. *Not rewarding yourself.*
   Homemakers are notorious for denying themselves pleasure and reward. This only leads to feeling neglected. Don't neglect yourself. Take the ten-minute break. You'll be

surprised at how it boosts your day.

2. *Over-rewarding yourself.* We often neglect to reward ourselves because we fear overindulging. Sometimes that's a legitimate fear. So give yourself a boundary—*one* square of your favorite chocolate, exactly ten minutes of phone chat with a good friend. If you overdo it occasionally, just start over the next day. The point is to establish the habit of flow.

 ### *Morning Snacks*

It's 10:30. If you haven't eaten since breakfast, it's probably getting hard to focus or be present. We don't always notice this. We are so used to being distracted, fidgety, and busy that we think it's normal. It's not. Stop and refresh yourself with a snack and a stretch.

First, the snack. My favorite morning snack is a handful of raw nuts plus one square of dark chocolate, and a glass of water. The nuts are all about "protein in the morning = energy all day." Also the natural fat from walnuts, almonds, and cashews helps me lose belly fat.

My other easy option is a CLIF Builder's Protein Bar. My personal favorite flavors are chocolate peanut butter, chocolate mint, and cookies-and-cream. Yay, chocolate is a friend! These bars sport 270 calories, so I usually eat half when I first feel the hunger about 10:00 or so, and then the other half by 11:00. There are many brands of protein bars, but there are also some stupid chemical bars pretending to be healthy. I like CLIF Bars. I like their ingredient list, I like their organic-ness, and I like Gary Erickson, the company founder. He has a great philosophy of business that favors back roads over ten-lane freeways.

Florence's Hearty Apple and Oat Scones

Florence's healthy scones are not as flaky as her buttery ones, but they have that same wholesome goodness charged up with oats, flax, and nuts. I love these and they keep my body happily nourished for several hours.

<u>Dry Mix</u>
½ cup whole wheat flour
1/3 cup buckwheat flour
½ cup + 3 Tbsp. old fashioned oats
2 Tbsp. natural brown cane sugar
¼ cup toasted pecans, coarsely chopped
1 Tbsp. ground flax seeds (optional)
½ tsp. cinnamon
1 tsp. baking powder
1/3 tsp. baking soda
¼ tsp. salt

<u>Wet Mix</u>
¾ stick cold unsalted butter, cut into small cubes

1 Granny Smith apple (unpeeled), coarsely grated
1/3 cup buttermilk

<u>Garnish</u>
Raw turbinado sugar (optional)

Mix all the dry ingredients together in a medium size bowl. Add in cold butter and, using your fingers, quickly rub the butter into the dry mixture until it resembles coarse crumbs.

Add apples and buttermilk and stir just enough for the dough to come together.

Turn dough onto a lightly floured surface. Pat dough into a rectangle of about 6" x 8". Cut into 6 squares. At this point the formed scones can be refrigerated for 3-4 days until ready to bake, or frozen for one month.

Preheat the oven to 400º. Place scones on a baking sheet lined with parchment paper or a silicone pastry mat. Brush tops with buttermilk and sprinkle with raw turbinado sugar (if using). Bake for 20-22 minutes. Cool before serving. The baked scones will keep at room temperature for one day.
© Florence Quinn 2012

Happiness Recipe 3: Stretch Yourself

By 10:30 most mornings, we've already been sitting for three hours. In fact, most Americans who work at desk jobs sit for 91% of their waking hours. Ninety-one percent! Think about it. We sit when we commute. We sit at desks or in meetings all day. And when we get home, what do we do? Um... sit. After all, we're exhausted from all that sitting!

Strange as it sounds, that's actually true. Human Performance Institute's exercise physiologist, Chris Jordan, taught me that sitting *is* exhausting because we sit on our biggest muscle. You know the one I mean. This constricts blood flow, which allows toxic CO_2 build up. Which leads to mental fog, decreased energy, and muscle tension. Sitting for long periods is now correlated with a shorter life span.

Our bodies are simply not designed for so much sitting. And going to the gym doesn't make up for it. Sitting for stretches of over an hour is what's killing us.

So by 10 or 10:30, it's time to move and, especially, stretch.

Science confirms that simple stretching will do more than increase your oxygen uptake and relieve tensed-up muscles. It will also improve your confidence, give you an endorphin rush, and help protect your body from injury.

But only if you actually make it a habit.

Dr. Ben Kim keeps a blog (*www.drbenkim.com*) filled with disarmingly simple advice on how to improve our health, one day at a time. He tells us that stretching promotes:

- Healthy blood flow and fluid exchange, which keep your muscles well-nourished and relatively free of buildup of waste products.
- More efficient exchange of nutrients and waste products at a cellular level, leading to better overall cellular function and inter-cellular communication.
- Lengthening of short (tight) muscles, tendons, and ligaments.

Even one bend-and-touch-your-toes stretch can make you feel like someone just gave you a compliment. How? By releasing endorphins into your bloodstream.

It's science, and it feels good—try it!

Or try this one. Clasp your hands behind your back. Then bend forward at the waist, stretching your arms away from your back. Hold that position for several seconds. Ahhh.

Is your lower back killing you? Are your joints stiff at the end of the day? Do you get migraines from the strain in your neck? Bad posture and stagnant muscles are probably the culprit.

By practicing a few simple stretches each day, you may be able to relieve your body of chronic pain. Dr. Kim says that when we are feeling pain or stiffness, most of us tend to reach out for medical treatment, such as painkillers, surgery, acupuncture, or chiropractic adjustments. Often, the simpler and more effective solution is just to improve blood circulation around the affected areas. By stretching. The majority of back pain, he says, is caused by too-tight muscles.

Stretching isn't just for people who are already battling chronic pain—it's for anyone who wants to increase productivity, become more motivated, and feel refreshed throughout the day.

Stretching four times a day, five to seven minutes per session, will brighten your health and happiness. Get a phone headset, because conference calls can also be a great opportunity to do some stretches. (At least *something* of value will be accomplished!)

Yoga: Stretch Yourself Into Happiness
I live in one of the yoga capitals of the U.S. It's near the beach in north San Diego County, and there are more yoga studios than restaurants. Everyone in the neighborhood seems very mellow. Of course, it may be the weather, but

I'm guessing it's the yoga.

The word yoga means "union," signifying a unifying of your mind-body-spirit. It has been practiced for over 5,000 years, and brain science is now discovering why it promotes so many benefits. For instance, many professional athletes are adopting yoga because it improves physical recovery, flexibility, strength, balance, and mental focus. Yoga is also used by more and more super-stressed workers, who benefit from its integrative health effect. Yoga uses mindful concentration, focused stretching, and regulated breathing to increase feelings of vitality and calmness as well as physical flexibility and stamina. It's all ignited by calm focus, breathing, muscle contraction, and employing a full range of motion for your body.

Awesome. So why aren't we all doing it?

Well, once you get over the woo-woo of any East-Indian-by-way-of-California-spiritual-exercise, it's time and convenience that stop most of us. We simply don't have a spare hour and a convenient place to practice. So here's a solution that just may be your answer. Our ThoughtRocket team named it "Instant Yoga." It takes 15 minutes to do, and is designed to maximize yoga's benefits for people without a lot of time. It has a distinctively American flavor, and you can do it anywhere without breaking a sweat. In fact, we filmed a session at a Gap store in San Diego that you can follow along with. To help busy Gap managers tune-up their vitality, our yogini designed the poses to focus on six things.

1. Mindful connection with the present moment
2. Strength of body and mind
3. Deep self-awareness
4. Alignment and confidence
5. Creativity and brain agility
6. Mind-body harmony

Yes, all this in less than 15 minutes a day.

Now, you don't have to work at Gap to get these benefits.

If you are interested in stretching your stretching into something more, go to *http://www.thoughtrocket.com/true-happiness* and click Instant Yoga. You'll memorize this short routine in just a few sessions, and you'll be able to do it anywhere.

 HAPPINESS RECIPE 3: Stretch and Smile

Trigger
Fatigue, feelings of overwhelm, frustration, pessimism. Sitting at your desk for more than an hour or two.

Response
Stand up, move, stretch... No, I mean *really* stretch. Try the Instant Yoga routine above, or visit a few stretching

websites to find some stretches that really work for *you*. Some good ones are:

- Mayo Clinic Workplace Exercises - *http://www.mayoclinic.com/health/stretching/WL0 0030*
- Stretches to Help You Sleep Better Tonight - *http://www.fitnessmagazine.com/workout/express/ 10-minute/stretches-to-help-you-sleep/*

If you want to add a mood bonus, try smiling as you stretch. For some wonderful reason, smiling with both your mouth and your eyes stimulates mood-elevating brain chemicals. I'm not kidding about this. Psychologists discovered that people who get Botox injections that stretch their faces into a faint "Joker"-like smile actually produce more mood-elevating neurotransmitters in their bloodstreams than they did before the injection. It seems that even artificially-induced, for-no-reason-at-all smiling makes us more optimistic and grateful. What's great about this is that you don't need to pump poisonous Botox (literally, *botulinum toxin*) into your face. Just smile. Be happy. To make smiling a habit, smile every time you stretch. This will brighten your day and strengthen your immune system.

If you want to make stretching a habit, here's what I suggest.

1. Set reminders on your phone to alert you to stretch at 10:00, 12:00, 3:00, and 8:00. Choose stretching routines that work the muscles most cramped or fatigued by *your* particular work style. For most

people, these include shoulders and neck, arms, forearms, wrists, and fingers (for those who type). You should also work your back, hamstrings, and calves, because sitting shortens, stiffens, and tightens all of those muscles. Try both static stretching, where you hold a stretch for fifteen to thirty seconds, and dynamic stretching, which involves continuous stretching movements.

Stretch every sixty minutes on plane flights or train rides. If a meeting is going too long, get up, move to the back of the room, and stretch away. The people you admire, and those who like you, will think it's cool. They may even join you! Finally, do your evening stretches about an hour before bed. This will help you sleep. Stretching is easy to do while watching television, and it creates a pre-sleep ritual that tells your mind-body to get ready to sleep.

2. Once you establish the times and circumstances that work for you, get your stretching routine down. Select a series of stretches that gently stretch your muscles without causing post-stretch pain. We are all designed a little differently, so some stretches may cause you chronic soreness. Once you have a good routine, memorize it in a simple order so it becomes an engrained habit. (If you choose Instant Yoga for your stretch session, this should be done at a time when you are free of distractions, so you get the full benefits of mindfulness.)

3. Enjoy the payoff:

Payoff
Feelings of exhilaration, a sense of mastery, stamina, alertness, and optimism. Increased energy and flexibility.

 X-Change

If you think this habit would make a big difference in your life right now, download my free calendar template and mark a big red X through every day you complete your habit. Give yourself a nice red X for every day that you stretch at least once. Later, you can increase the requirements for earning an X to two, three, or four stretch sessions a day. Make a string of 7 X's to see how this habit works for you. And if you decide to make it permanent, keep that string of X's going!

And join people just like you at the Thought Rocket community. Tell us what's working for you. We'd especially like to hear your responses to Instant Yoga. The main thing is to encourage, inspire, ask questions. (*http://www.thoughtrocket.com/true-happiness*)

Special Habits for Moms or Dads Who Are Domestic Engineers
Kids love moving. They also love imitating. Get them in on your stretching routine, and

you can feel good about helping them create a habit that will do them good their entire lives.

If they lose interest, or start begging you to do something else, narrate the reason for your stretches as you go. "Do you like it when Mommy pushes you in the swing? This stretch will help Mommy push you really high!" "Do you like it when Daddy gives you a piggy-back ride? This stretch makes Daddy's back strong, so he can carry you all day." Watch their attitude change when they realize how what you're doing will make *them* happy.

 Flavored Water Recipes

The Best Water on Earth
It's vitally important to drink water, all day long. That doesn't mean it needs to be tasteless or colorless. It can in fact be yummy, which is exactly how Monica Methany (*http://www.theyummylife.com*) makes it. She only uses water, ice, fruit, herbs, and a jar. Her recipes take about two minutes to mix up, but will make you feel refreshed all day long. Monica recommends fresh fruit when it's in season, frozen fruit otherwise. (Frozen fruit that's picked ripe has more flavor and nutrients than weird, fresh-

looking fruit flown in from who knows where.)

Monica's water recipes are made in two-quart mason jars with plastic lids. These are easy to take to work and store in a fridge. By the way, when she talks about "bruising" fruit or herbs, she means gently mashing them a bit with a wooden spoon, or with an odd thing called a muddler. Bruising releases flavors into the water.

Here are Monica's yummy waters:

Citrus Flavored Water

> Slice 1 orange, 1 lime, 1 lemon into rounds, then cut the rounds in half. Add to jar, press with the handle of a wooden spoon. Press enough to release some of the juices, but don't pulverize the fruit into pieces. Fill the jar with ice. Pour in water to the top. Stir it with the handle of a wooden spoon or a chopstick. Put a lid on it, put it in the fridge, and chill.
>
> The flavor intensifies if it's made an hour or two before you drink it. It's even better the next day. The ice at the top serves as a sieve, so that you can pour the flavored water without getting fruit bits in your glass.

Raspberry Lime Flavored Water

> Quarter 2 limes. With your hand, squeeze the juice into the jar, then throw in the squeezed lime

quarters. Add raspberries. Press and twist to release some of the juices (don't pulverize the fruit). Fill the jar with ice, then add water to the top. Stir, cover, and refrigerate.

Pineapple Mint Flavored Water

Add a sprig of mint to the jar—you can throw in the whole sprig or remove the leaves from the sprig, if you prefer to have the mint swimming around in the jar. Bruise the leaves and release their flavor—don't pulverize them into bits. Add pineapple pieces, press, and twist to release juices. Add ice to the top and then water. Stir, cover, and refrigerate.

Blackberry Sage Flavored Water

Add sage leaves to jar and bruise. Add blackberries; press and twist to release their juices. Fill jar with ice cubes, add water to the top, stir, cover, and refrigerate.

Watermelon Rosemary Flavored Water

Add a sprig of rosemary to jar and muddle gently (rosemary releases a strong flavor without much muddling). Add watermelon cubes; twist and press gently to release juices. Fill jar with ice cubes, add water to the top, stir, cover, and refrigerate.

How long will they keep? Put a lid on them, stick them in the fridge, and they will keep for up to three days. It only takes a few minutes to make several varieties to keep on hand. No more boring water for me!

Happiness Recipe 4: Turn On Your Superpower - Learn What You Love

What does learning have to do with happiness? Science tells us that humans are *designed* to learn, grow, and evolve to a more capable state. Healthy humans sense their own potential and seek to fulfill it. Thus, any action we take toward learning generates an inner sense of well-being. We respect ourselves more. We become more hopeful.

This happens most powerfully when we focus our learning on what deeply interests us and what we are naturally good at. Our innate talents scream to be developed, especially when our talents are inspired by our personal purpose. Then they become "motivated talents." Superpowers for TRUE work and TRUE play.

Our ThoughtRocket happiness research clearly shows that playing to your strengths allows you to succeed without over-stressing, and to intrinsically enjoy the work you do. This leads to work that *gives* you energy, rather than saps it from you.

That is vital, if you are serious about pursuing happiness.

Today, it isn't enough to be good at something. In fact, the future has no need of generic workers. As my colleague Dr. Joe Folkman says, "To create value and be valued in the 21st century we need to be extraordinary." And there is only one sure way we can be extraordinary. That's finding and fulfilling our TRUE work. Work that is a reflection of our authentic best. Work that motivates us to gain expertise and create genuine value.

Here's the point. Extraordinary excellence doesn't come when you try to excel at things you aren't good at or don't deeply care about. Dancing comes to mind for me. It's just not something I should do in public. Likewise, my work requires me to do many things I am not very good at, and never will be. Travel details, for instance, or making others follow a process—these are things I am magnificently mediocre at.

As I have matured, I've quit trying to pretend I'm good at things I'm not . I've also developed a clear sense of what I am willing to learn and master, and what I am content to let others do.

Remember, I've said that your TRUE work, the work that will make you the happiest and most successful, uses your *Talent* at a very high level. Because it flows from your core being, it is also intrinsically *Rewarding*. Your TRUE work enables you to create value for others via your *Unique* form of self-expression. And it spurs you to *Evolve* by being and doing your best.

So here is how to bring that to life.

First, make a commitment to learn something that fascinates you, and learn it to the point of mastery. If the learning is intrinsically magnetic to you, you know you're onto something. If you find you're making time to learn more, and are telling others about it, you are coming face to face with your motivated talent.

Second, study the industry or profession you think you'd like to play in. Become intensely knowledgeable about the trends, challenges, and opportunities of the industry. If that captures you, you have found your playground. That means it's the profession or industry that empowers your TRUE purpose. A brilliant biochemist could work for a tobacco company, or at a cancer research lab. Choosing the positive value you wish to create must be intentional. If either the specialized knowledge or the characteristics of the industry fail to float your boat, keep looking. When you find your TRUE work, and use your superpower to serve a personal purpose, happiness rises like a hang glider on a warm thermal.

Your TRUE work also supercharges your learning. When we are learning what we intrinsically value, we are unafraid to fail. In fact, we naturally push ourselves to our limits and beyond, because that's where growth occurs. You've probably experienced this when learning a loved sport like skiing, or pushing your guitar skills to the next level.

Learning skills that you value and enjoy is a mind-expanding act. This can even happen in the context of your daily work—provided you approach it like learning a loved hobby. You can make learning a habit by choosing to master new skills that create the value you are uniquely designed for. As a bonus, it will also change your mind... yes, biologically.

Redesigning Our Brains to Learn

You are a complex, self-regulating system. And that is awesome. The brilliant Dr. Daniel Siegel, who has spent his life studying the connections between our bodies, our brains, and our happiness, tells us that our great source of power is our ability to select new information and consciously redesign our brains to regulate our emotions. This ability is called neuroplasticity. Yep, as in plastic brain. We can reshape our brains' ability to learn what we want to learn, and also to help our emotions feel what we want to feel. How? Through focused attention, exercise, and new knowledge or experience.

Siegel's research at UCLA indicates that putting focused attention on what's happening in the present moment turns nearly everything into a brain-expanding experience. On the other hand, maintaining a closed mind, coupled with a daily routine of thoughtless habits, makes us duller and more stressed.   It turns out mental agility, or *adaptability*, is central to our happiness. It is also the key to learning everything we need in order to fulfill our authentic selves.

 HAPPINESS RECIPE 4: Turn On Your Superpower

Trigger
Anytime you feel inspired to do better because you love what you are doing. Anytime you feel disappointed with your performance or frustrated that your present work is drudgery.

Response
You already love to acquire new knowledge and improve skills that relate to your TRUE work. You just need to become conscious of it, and invest yourself in it. Here's how:

1. Notice what parts of your work *give* you energy. What things do you do that make you lose track of time? Be specific. Cultivate an awareness of all the activities that bring you natural joy and satisfaction.
2. Mindfully choose something you'd like to develop expertise in. It should be something you value and enjoy.

3. Get a clear sense of what you already know in this area, and what you *want* to know in order to get better.

4. Set aside at least 20-30 minutes each day to do something (read, watch a video, interview a mentor) to accelerate your learning. Today, we are surrounded by a cornucopia of ways to learn. The Google web can bring up inspiring TED talks on any subject we are interested in. We can view funny how-to videos. We can listen to podcasts and webinars with thought leaders. In the brick-and-mortar world, we can make appointments with mentors and ask them questions like "How did you learn to _____ so well?" We can also read books or trade publications. The main thing is to focus your mind on value-rich learning, not just on randomly consuming information that you are not deeply interested in.

5. Next, learn by doing. Volunteer for a work project that interests you, one that will put you in a little over your head. Make yourself uncomfortable; this will stimulate your creativity and work your learning muscles.

6. Start using your new learning to achieve goals. Embrace the do-fail-learn cycle by considering what it was like to master walking. It's estimated that one-year-olds fall down over 500 times before they walk. At one time, you were that undaunted. Reclaim that enthusiasm. Above all, don't worry about being perfect. If you'd been a perfectionist about learning to walk, you'd still be crawling.

Perfection is death to creative effort, which is at the heart of the joy of learning.

7. Take stock of your learning every thirty days. On the first of every month, ask yourself what you have learned—*that you love*—over the past thirty days.

If You Want To Flourish...
Keep a Flourish Journal. This is a simple exercise, popularized by Dr. Martin Seligman. Simply ask yourself what are three things you did well that you enjoyed over the past 24 hours. Write the answers down. In 21 days, you will see a pattern of things you do when you're flourishing. These are the things you want to do more of.

For instance, I flourish when I am well prepared, patient and focused on others' interests. This is good to know, because I tend to wing it and push my own agenda. Self-knowledge about what personal behaviors bring you success and joy, and what you do that is self-defeating is golden.

Payoff
Imagine what you might be able to do a year from now, if you spent 30 minutes a day learning something you love that's relevant to your TRUE work. Just imagine it. What we really desire is not perfection itself; it's peace, fulfillment, and a sense of endless growth. We get these feelings from what William Faulkner called our "splendid

failures," as well as our enjoyable successes. We get them by milking joy from every opportunity to learn and contribute our best. And from the excitement of knowing there will be more opportunities when we wake up tomorrow.

 X-Change

Increasingly, our world values "extreme experts." People who know a lot about something that excites them. People who can do something extremely skillfully. Happily, this is also something we value in ourselves. Knowledge and skill give us confidence, and encourage our self-expression. Both are ingredients in our happiness. When you make a habit of learning a little bit each day, this will lead to mastery. You don't need to find lots of extra time to master something you love. You already have 20 minutes every day, maybe even 30. Just start.

If you think this daily learning habit would make a big difference in your life right now, download my free calendar template. Mark a big red X through every day you spend at least 20 minutes (the length of a TED talk) doing something (anything) to increase your learning as it relates to your TRUE work or TRUE play. Make a string of 7 X's to see how this habit works for you. And if you decide to make it permanent, keep that string of X's going!

If you want to make learning both stimulating and more

fun, join us at ThoughtRocket community and find others who want to learn what you do. Share ideas. Create a new learning network. Make learning enjoyable.

And comment on the thread below! Tell the ThoughtRocket community what's working for you! Encourage, inspire, ask questions.
(*http://www.thoughtrocket.com/true-happiness*)

Special Habit for Moms or Dads Who Are Domestic Engineers

It's easy for devoted homemakers to feel that their entire identity is submerged in the role of spouse/parent. So take a few minutes to reconnect with something you really enjoyed when you used to have time for it, whether it was a recreational activity or a career path. Reengage with that skill or activity via the Internet. Email an author or artist you admire. Try making a personal connection.   Join a blogging group, where you can trade ideas with other enthusiasts. Just knowing that there are others out there who appreciate your input will kick your creativity back in gear.

Happiness Recipe 5: Half-Time: Play, Refresh, Connect

Ever wonder why so many sports have a half-time? The players head to the locker room to rest, talk, make strategic adjustments, and refocus on the second half. Most games are won in the second half.

Perhaps we should learn to look at our workdays that way. According to the U.S. Department of Commerce, studies show that human productivity peaks for 6.1 hours of work, then drops off a cliff. A university study showed that after seven weeks, two similar groups doing the exact same work produced exactly the same output, even though one group worked forty hours a week and the other worked fifty. It seems we all have a productivity set-point. We are going to hit a high rate of excellence for only so many hours in a day, no matter how many hours we work.

So... we should really make our high-impact hours count.

That means amplifying our productivity by producing more value with the same or less effort. This requires taking a *daily* vacation from work. When you renew yourself in very intentional ways, you can literally refresh your entire mind-body.

Remember, the renowned Cooper Clinic projects that 52% of managers working today will die from stress caused by their work. This is why. The way we work today is toxic to us. When former President Lyndon Johnson died at 64, historian Doris Kearns Goodwin asked her Harvard psychologist friend Erik Erikson what he thought was the reason. Erikson replied that LBJ's work style probably killed him. Johnson had a habit of working 100% of the time he was awake. And he slept very little. He persisted in this engrained habit even when he retired. Erikson said the happiest and healthiest people he'd studied had a healthy mix of work, love, and play in their life every day! The three passions, all in harmony.

How many people do you know have that? A healthy mix of work, love, and play in their lives. Every day. Do you?

It was Ronald Reagan, another former U.S. President, who said, "Hard work never killed anyone... but why take a chance?" He famously watched movies instead of reading State Department briefings and went to bed at 9:30 every night. He lived until he was 93.

I'm not saying work is bad. I *am* saying the way most of us work is stupid. We make our work harder than it needs to be. We sabotage our own productivity. That's because we have lost the natural rhythm of work, love and play in our lives. And it's making us sick. Perhaps the saddest thing of all is that over 80% of managers responding to a large-scale survey can't name a single active hobby or passion that regularly brings them joy.

The Wisdom of Half-Time

To restore sanity to their work lives, I've helped scores of people institute a half-time habit for their game of work. Half-time is noon.

In today's frenzied work culture, many people work through lunch. They eat at their desk, checking their emails or preparing for meetings. If that sounds like you— if you wolf down your food without tasting it as you blast out emails—please stop it! Or if you have frequent business lunches that combine eating with business, please don't.

When you have been working all morning, what you need at lunch is half-time. A break from work to refresh your brain and your body. A genuine time-out to let your business-brain rest and regroup, to assimilate what's happened, and to prepare to refocus for the workday's second half.

Here is why. Have you ever studied something so hard and so long that new information seems to bounce off? I know I have. I study and learn, study and learn, until I feel my brain is overstuffed. Further study is fruitless in those moments. Our brain needs to assimilate what we've input. It needs to connect the dots of the new information with old knowledge. It's our brain's *ability to synthesize* our life experience, skills, and knowledge with new information that gives us that rarest of all human qualities—wisdom. This is what wakes the Yoda within.

The great Dr. Herbert Benson of Harvard Medical School studied the biological roots of insight, which is the driver of game-changing innovation. He found that overly long periods of concentration blind us to new, simpler answers. Our brains tend to work stressful problems over and over in our left temporal lobe. This part of our brain puts our thoughts on train tracks that lead us nowhere new.

Benson found that to invite better, quicker, and simpler solutions we need to relax. That means turning our attention to an entirely different activity. Ideally, something fun. It's this alternating rhythm of focus and fun that stimulates our whole brain to discover answers we never thought of.

When we take a true half-time break, we engage our right temporal lobe by doing something we enjoy or socializing with friends. This allows our unconscious to get an aerial view of the landscape of our problem. This wider view rises above the non-essential issues and old assumptions, and glimpses new, simpler answers—the "a-ha's" that change everything. These are the bright ideas we often get when we are out on a walk, taking a shower, or talking to a friend.

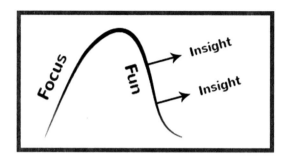

So the paradox of productivity is that working less can enable you to create more value. If you relax your grip on your challenges, you'll discover how to do hard things more easily.

The bottom line is that if we are going to do great work, our brain needs to play. This means we need a complete getaway from what we're working on so we can refresh and reboot. That's why we *need* a daily half-time. This should be a complete one-hour vacation from work. And you shouldn't feel guilty about it. You are simply giving your brain the conditions it requires to achieve excellence. If you do it right, you will return from your hour vacation refreshed and recharged, ready to make your second half a rip-roaring success.

Spend Half-Time with Others
So what do you *do* at half-time? Anything you enjoy. Anything that's a TRUE getaway. Anything that absorbs your attention in an intrinsically pleasurable way. You could be like Robin, who decided to take up sketching. She breaks away most days at lunch, goes outside, and pencil-sketches a scene. This has woken up a whole new part of

her analytical brain. Most workdays, she is immersed in spreadsheets, doing financial data mining. Now, every day, she suddenly has a wonderful vacation smack dab in the middle of it. Something to look forward to. Something that primes her for the rest of her business day.

That said, let me suggest the ultimate half-time activity: connecting with friends.

Social scientists tell us we live in an age of increasing social isolation. Though many of us have over 300 Facebook friends, we have fewer *intimate* friends than we did even a generation ago. Friends we can trust with our deep secrets. Friends who "see" our true motives, not just our behavior. Friends who tell us the truth, even when it hurts a little. Friends who inconvenience themselves just to hang out with us. Friends who would miss us for the rest of their lives if we died. That kind of friend.

These days we are too busy to have true, committed friends. Being busy prevents us from building the loyalty and trust that comes from spending time together. Not just "quality" time, but good old-fashioned "hanging out."

You, Me, and We

Do you have a best friend who "gets" you? Someone who just seems to understand how you feel? Someone you don't have to explain yourself to?

We now know the biological basis for this type of

mutual understanding. Brain scientists have identified something they call mirror neurons. These brain cells actually pick up the intentions, feelings, and even thoughts of others. They're like little antenna dishes that tune in on others' frequencies.

Dr. Dan Siegel says they're what make emotions as contagious as yawns. They're what allow friends and close couples to finish each other's sentences. I experience this all the time with my wife, Debbie. We'll be riding in the car, and I'll start thinking about something completely unrelated to our current conversation. She'll switch to my new subject before I've said a word about it.

Thoughts are energy and information. We don't need a biological connection to exchange them. We don't need words, either. All we need is presence. Our full presence *amplifies* our thoughts. That's why just thinking loving, affirming thoughts toward others creates goodwill. And that's why the opposite is also true.

What does this have to do with productivity? Plenty. Because it's also true that one of the key markers of fulfilling work is having a "best friend" on the job. A friend you can confide in, have fun with, laugh with, and enjoy. Yet most of us are too busy working to "waste time" with friends.

121

We can change that with half-time. A great half-time activity is eating lunch with your best friend at work (brown bagging is expected), then going for a walk-and-talk. If you really want to be bad—in a good way—take a long lunch and go to a matinee movie once a month, or go shopping together, or take a noon cooking class. Playing hooky makes for great bonding. It may also spring loose a new idea that solves a nagging problem. Just have some positive, shared experiences, and open your heart and mind to someone you like, trust, and respect.

Remember, Erikson said that happy, healthy people have a *daily dose* of work, love, and play in their lives. I think we've always known that. What we *didn't* know, until we started looking at brain scans, is that love and play enable us to be wiser, more productive, and more focused performers. That's TRUE happiness at its core.

So are you ready to make a healthy, daily half-time a habit?

 HAPPINESS RECIPE 5: Half-Time

Trigger
Lunchtime. Or anytime you feel overwhelmed and overstressed from a long stretch of work.

Response
Each weekday, plan a positive, hour-long lunch break to

122

start a new, true hobby or resurrect an old one. Meet up with friends, or use the time to develop new ones. Walk, talk, take a short class, play a game together... be creative. I know a busy senior manager who hangs with her self-created knitting club to "stitch and bitch" for an hour (her description). Start a lunchtime book club, or join one. The point is, do something you enjoy with *someone* you enjoy every workday. Even chatting and chewing lunch together is good. Make a habit of refreshing yourself at half-time.

If you are a solo worker or work at home, the same habit can be formed. If it's too hard to meet a friend in person, connect via Skype, iChat, or FaceTime, or just call a friend or family member and get caught up. Engage in your hobbies. At minimum, go for a walk out of your home. Break away, read your novel, watch a show you've recorded. Once a week, do something you really, really enjoy. It might be a quick museum visit to see a new exhibit, or test-driving a car you can't afford. Create a solid hour to refresh your brain and your emotions.

Your TRUE Play
Refreshing play follows the TRUE recipe—Talent, Reward, Uniqueness, and Evolution.

If you're not sure what your true play is, welcome to the club. Our research shows 80% of us don't have any hobbies or interests we are passionately engaged in. It seems we've forgotten how to play. This is how I help people discover their TRUE play:

1. Just Start: Try different things out. Take action. Go to a hot air balloon festival. Take a mini-course in archery. Try making sushi. Throw your whole self into something new that attracts you. If it gives you juice, keep at it. If not, try something else.
2. Engage Experts: Learn from the best. Read, watch instructional videos, or get lessons to help you succeed faster.
3. Strive for Excellence: TRUE play engages your natural desire to get better. So if you're enjoying improving, keep improving.

One more thing. You may not discover a personal hobby you love for a whole lifetime. That's fine. Life has seasons. Change your play anytime you feel the urge.

Play daily. Embrace joy. It'll make you better at everything.

Payoff

Less stress, better work. Your life will also begin to take on a deeper harmony. You will be more resilient for dealing with unexpected challenges. Your afternoon will be more productive and creative, and your evening more enriched. Your life will suck much less.

X-Change

If you think half-time would make a big difference in your life right now, download my free calendar template and mark a big red X through every day you take a one-hour vacation at lunch time. Make a string of 21 X's to see how this habit works for you. And if you decide to make it permanent, keep that string of X's going!

And tell our ThoughtRocket community what you are doing. Tell us about a time when you got a breakthrough insight by turning away from your problem and let your inner wisdom find a new answer. Let us know how you discovered your TRUE play. And the more ideas we can generate to inspire better half-times, the better for all of us. Share your life at *http://www.thoughtrocket.com/true-happiness.*

Special Habit for Moms or Dads Who Are Domestic Engineers
The world of domestic engineering can have just as many superficial connections as a regular office environment. You might see the same group of parents every day at the park or the preschool, but do you know about their lives—not just about their kids' potty-training history?

Try asking fellow parents or caregivers questions that are about them personally, not just about them as a parent. What did you study in college? Where did you grow up? Find a real connection with someone and take your kids on an outing that the grownups will appreciate, too—a museum, the beach, or even just exploring a different neighborhood. Create a meaningful "half-time" that you can really look forward to.

 ## *Half-time Recipes*

SALADS

I used to think salads came in a bag at the supermarket. Then I met Florence and Heather, and salads transformed into fun food. These delicious lunches can be made ahead of time, stored in your fridge, and transported to work via a plastic storage container. They are well worth the effort.

Florence's Bean & Baby Potato Salad with Feta and Dill

A very refreshing, nutritious, multi-colored salad that can be assembled in minutes (serves 2 as a main dish or 6 as a side).

1 dozen baby potatoes, unpeeled
1 large handful green beans, stems removed
½ can kidney beans, rinsed well
1/3 cup feta cheese, crumbled
2 Tbsp. fresh dill, chopped
1 lemon, juice and zest
2 Tbsp. extra virgin olive oil
Fleur de sel (or any good salt) and freshly
ground black pepper, to taste
¼ cup sliced almonds, toasted

Place the potatoes in a medium saucepan, cover
with water, bring to a boil, reduce to simmer and
cook for about 10-12 minutes or until cooked
through but still firm. Drain and allow to cool. Cut
into quarters.

Bring a large pot of water to a boil. Add a good
tablespoon of salt. When water has reached a full
boil, add the green beans. Cook for about 7-8
minutes or until cooked through but still firm and
bright green. Drain and immediately place in an ice
bath (a bowl filled with cold water and ice cubes) to
stop the cooking process. Once cooled, drain and
set aside.

In a large bowl, combine potatoes, green beans,
kidney beans, feta, and dill. Make the dressing in a
small jar by combining lemon juice and zest, olive
oil, salt and pepper. Toss vegetables with dressing,
taste, and adjust seasoning if necessary. Add the

almonds last and serve immediately.
© Florence Quinn 2012

Heather's Egg Salad

12 large organic eggs, hard boiled
2 Tbsp. organic mayonnaise, vegan dressing (like Nayonaise), or olive oil-based mayo
1 Tbsp. organic whole-grain mustard
2 stalks organic celery, washed and chopped
1 small organic dill pickle, washed and chopped
¼ organic red onion, washed and chopped
1 Tbsp. lemon juice
¼ tsp. garlic powder
Sea salt and pepper to taste

Peel the eggs and place them in a glass mixing bowl. Mash them coarsely with a potato masher (or just cut them into chunks). Add other ingredients and mix well.

Heather's Chicken Salad with Pistachios

1 lb. grilled chicken, diced
½ yellow bell pepper, diced
½ large fennel bulb, diced
¼ red onion, soaked in lemon juice for 10 minutes
⅓ cup pistachios
1 Tbsp. fresh thyme, minced
¼ jar Lemonaise, or to taste (can be found at most health food and specialty food stores)

Splash of rice wine vinegar and/or apple cider vinegar
Splash of olive oil
Kosher salt and fresh ground pepper to taste

Combine all ingredients in a large bowl and mix well. Season to taste.

Heather's Artichoke & Tuna Salad

This is super easy and simply great.

6 ounces cooked tuna, flaked (or 1 can tuna in water, drained)
1 cup chopped canned artichoke hearts
½ cup chopped olives
2 tsp. lemon juice
2 Tbsp. olive oil-based mayonnaise
1½ tsp. chopped fresh oregano, or ½ teaspoon dried

Combine in bowl and serve.

Florence's Farro and Vegetable Salad with Yogurt Dressing

From Florence: "If you have never had farro, you are in for a treat. The grains (or berries, to be precise) look a little like brown rice and can be cooked like it—pre-soaking will cut cooking time by half. They have a deliciously rich, nutty flavor and a pleasant, chewy

*texture. In this recipe, farro complements fresh
vegetables and a tangy dressing that make a wonderful
salad for a summer lunch."*

(Serves 4 as a main course.)

<u>Salad</u>
2 cups cooked farro
1 cup fennel, shaved
½ cup carrot, shaved
½ cup radishes, shaved
½ cup canned chickpeas, rinsed and drained
½ cup feta, crumbled
1 large handful arugula

<u>Dressing</u>
¼ cup milk or soy or almond milk
¼ cup plain yogurt
2 Tbsp. Dill, finely chopped
1 Tbsp. shallots, finely chopped
1 Tbsp. lemon juice, to taste
Salt and freshly ground black pepper, to taste

<u>Salad:</u>
Toss all the salad ingredients, except the feta and
arugula, in a large bowl.

<u>Dressing:</u>
Mix all the ingredients of the dressing in a small jar,
shake well, and adjust seasoning with lemon juice,
salt, and pepper if necessary.

Assembly:
Toss salad with dressing. Garnish with feta and arugula leaves.

© Florence Quinn 2012

SANDWICHES

Will's Tuscan Delight

Italians call great prosciutto, meat butter. For good reason. Also, it's cured without nitrites, which means it's a friend. You can get it at your deli, or the grocery store deli section. Get the best.

> Prosciutto, thinly sliced
> Sprouted whole grain bread, sliced
> Organic tomato, sliced
> ½ ripe avocado
> Organic yellow mustard
> Fresh lettuce
>
> Make into a quick sandwich and eat.

Will's Apple, Cheese, and Ham Sandwich

> 2 slices sprouted whole grain bread
> 1 slice Asiago cheese (Cheese is a fun food, like fudge. If you're not allergic to dairy, a little won't kill you, and it makes life worth loving.)
> Organic yellow mustard
> 1 slice uncured Black Forest ham

131

A few thin slices of a Granny Smith green apple
Dash of sea salt

*The apple makes the sandwich. Try it and taste what
I mean.*

*What about chips? Okay, okay, if you're one of those
who's saying "Come on, man, I've got to have a few
chips," here's what you do. Get a bag of Stacy's
baked pita chips. They're sprinkled with sea salt and
are super tasty. Eat 5-7 with your salad or sandwich
for 75 calories. You'll love yourself more than if you
oink out on those salty grease-crisps called potato
chips.*

Drew's Mona Lisa BLT

*Are you ready for Drew's Mona Lisa BLT? I'll let him tell you
about it.*

5 ounces organic arugula
3-4 ounces thinly sliced Italian pancetta
8 ounces sheep's milk ricotta
2 large tomatoes, sliced (¼ inch thick)
1 loaf walnut bread
Cultured butter
Fleur de sel
Freshly ground black pepper
Extra virgin olive oil
Freshly cut lemon, for juice
(Serves 4)

From Drew: "First, I prepare the organic arugula by putting it in a large mixing bowl and adding generous amounts of extra virgin Italian olive oil, fleur de sel (sea salt harvested by hand from the Mediterranean in Sicily), and freshly ground black pepper. I use tongs to thoroughly, but lightly, coat each leaf. I then add a few squeezes of lemon juice, mix, and let the arugula sit.

"Next, I slice a loaf of walnut bread, gray-purple in color, that has been baked that morning by my local French bakery. It is called a "miche de noix" and has an oblong, football shape, with a longitudinal diameter of 3-4 inches. The crust is hard, with the crispness of a good baguette, though a bit thicker, and the crumb (the soft, inner part of the bread) is generously populated with walnuts. I select twin slices of the bread for each sandwich. I spread one side generously with a locally produced cultured butter. The other side I cover with a quarter inch of a locally crafted sheep's milk ricotta cheese. Then I soak the ricotta with a 7-year aged balsamic vinegar imported from Italy.

"Meanwhile I cook thin slices of imported Italian pancetta on a cast-iron skillet heated to medium. The thinness is very important, as the pancetta is meant to complement the ricotta, not overwhelm it. (I choose pancetta over bacon for the same reason; to avoid the wonderful but overwhelming flavor of smoked pork.) I then remove the pancetta from the pan using tongs, leaving the fatty, rich juices in the skillet. Then, keeping the pan at the same temperature, I add the slices of tomato and pan-fry them in the pancetta drippings. I leave the tomatoes in for several minutes on the first side and about 1 minute on the second.

"While the tomatoes are in the pan, I add some fleur de sel, freshly ground black pepper, and extra virgin Italian olive oil, drizzled as needed. The tomatoes are finished when their flesh has a wilted and slightly browned appearance, and the very act of removing them from the pan by spatula causes them to lose structural integrity. I then place the tomato slices directly onto the ricotta side of the sandwich and finish with a bit more fleur de sel and ground black pepper, to taste.

"I place one thin slice of the cooked pancetta atop each tomato. Upon the buttered side, I heap a generous amount of the seasoned arugula, and serve the sandwich open-faced, to enhance the beauty of the dish. It is then eaten in the traditional manner—both halves put together. I enjoy imbibing a local, micro-brewed medium dark ale or porter with this meal."

Is he a character or what? No, I assure you that he actually makes his food this way, and feeds it to his very lucky family.

Happiness Recipe 6: Life Is a Gym

We are designed to be Italians. Or Spaniards. Any culture that takes a nap after lunch. Our natural biorhythms start slowing down at about 2 p.m. and continue to dip until about 3:00. Our mental alertness fades. Our problem-solving and analytic capabilities dim. Our creative edge gets duller and duller. Even our personalities retreat behind a wall of impatience and intolerance. Yep, we become a dumbed-down version of ourselves on most afternoons.

What can be done about it?

Well, if you can take a short nap at 2:00, please do so. Afternoon naps are highly correlated with greater health, lower weight, and longer life.

But if you are like me, taking an afternoon nap is often impractical. So it's a perfect time to recharge your energy with exercise.

A brisk walk will invigorate you nearly as much as a restful nap. If you enjoy going to a gym, taking yoga classes, or running for a few miles, and you can do so at 2 or 3 p.m., go for it. Yet most of us can't do that either. We still have work to do, and it's considered, ahem, bad form to engage in sweaty exercise for thirty minutes and then return, unwashed, to a civilized workplace.

So if a full vigorous workout is not practical, I suggest keeping your street clothes on and exercising in or around your office for a few recharging minutes.

A hundred years ago, before most of us had sit-down jobs, there were no gyms with monthly memberships and high-tech workout clothes. Instead, we had jobs that required daily exertion. That exertion kept us healthy. Nowadays, we need to build in exertion consciously.

Physical exercise sparks our life force. Exercise triggers a whole cascade of positive, happiness-promoting benefits. And remember, by exercise I simply mean brisk, intentional movement; you don't need to break a sweat.

Here is a short list of all the great things light exercise can do for you:
- **Improved Brain function:** Harvard's John Ratey has spent his professional life showing how exercise speeds up the neuro-networks of our brains. In fact, exercise can increase our brains' processing speed by as much as 350%. It also stimulates the growth of new brain cells that help with memory and problem solving. So exercise

makes us smarter. It's a clinical fact.

Ratey's studies reveal our brains get the biggest benefit from exercise that demands coordination. Ping-pong, yoga, Tai Chi, and dancing are examples.

- **Increased Optimism:** Exercise is like a hope pill. It stimulates our creative thinking centers. Increased oxygen empowers our capacity to create new solutions to persistent problems.
- **Weight Control:** Light exercise won't burn many calories, but it prompts us to make wiser and healthier choices around food. It seems to stimulate our resolve to eat nutritious food, in small amounts, more frequently.
- **Increased Confidence:** People who consciously exercise every day report feeling more confident in their ability to tackle tough problems and bounce back from disappointment. Keeping a daily commitment to intentionally move your body generates a sense of willpower, and can make you feel inspired.
- **More and Better Energy:** Naturally, exercise increases your *physical* energy, but according to the Human Performance Institute, it also improves your energy for high-level *emotions* like patience and enthusiasm. It increases *mental* energy, too, enabling you to focus for longer periods. HPI's research also confirms that it increases your conviction to stay true to your values and your

vision for your best life. Call that *spiritual* energy.

So the "pro" evidence for the benefits of exercise is overwhelming. But you probably already knew that. Then why aren't you doing it? If you're not regularly exercising, perhaps it's because you think you don't have time, or that it's no fun. Let's dispel those myths by creating an easy new habit.

This habit is called "Life Is a Gym." It means that you use every opportunity to move your body throughout the day. When you make it a habit, you'll start to move without thinking. Your mind-body begins to naturally desire to dance throughout the day, but especially around "sleepy time" at 3:00 pm. Some ideas to get you started are:

- Never, ever pass up a chance to climb stairs. Stair-climbing engages your large leg muscles and puts an immediate load on your heart. Climb as quickly as you are able. Two steps at a time is great, if you are feeling frisky. Hang loosely onto the handrail (you don't want to crash and smash).
- When you're on the phone or a conference call, jog in place. Here's how. Stand up, put your arms at your side, and lift your forearms, making a ninety-degree angle at your elbow. Face your palms downward and pump each leg up like you're high stepping. Touch your knees to your open palms. Do that for fifteen minutes and see how you feel.
- Do squats for your legs and buttocks. Again, any exercise using your large leg muscles will get your blood and oxygen pumping. You can start by just

standing up and sitting down in a chair. Do two sets of twelve of these puppies and you'll feel pumped.

Of course there are many, many ways to naturally engage in light exercise throughout every day. For instance, don't *email or text* your work colleagues—get up from your desk and go see them. When you go to Target, Trader Joe's, or any other store with a parking lot, park at the outer edge and walk briskly to the store. Most of us walk only about 3,300 steps a day. The American Heart Association tells us we can achieve a high level of heart health by taking 10,000 steps a day. A $10 pedometer clipped to your belt will count your steps for you. Just keeping track will motivate you to walk more.

My favorite daily light exercise is the walking meeting. I try to schedule a thirty-minute walking meeting every weekday. Sometimes it's with my colleagues or with a new business contact. Often it's with my wife, who runs my business operations along with our family operations.

The advantage of the thirty-minute walking meeting is that it's not only exercise, but it's also a relationship builder. Here's why. When you walk side by side with another person, it only takes about three minutes for your speed, cadence, and gait to become synchronized. As your bodies begin to move in sync, your brain waves do, too. There is a harmonizing, rapport-building effect. An additional bonus is that you're likely to be more transparent in your communication. Why? Because you are not looking directly into the face of your walking partner. Researchers have discovered that *not* seeing the 500 micro facial responses we make per minute allows us to be more candid and open.

As a dedicated afternoon walk-and-talker, I can personally attest to the relationship-building power, as well as the exercise benefits, of a daily walk-and-talk. And remember, if your walking partner isn't available in person, you can do a phone walk-and-talk. It works very well with headphones.

Once you become mindful about moving your body, you will see the world in a different way. So make movement at 3 o'clock an everyday habit. Your late afternoon (3:30-5:00) productivity will soar, which is like picking up an extra ninety minutes of quality time each day. You'll also begin to see huge happiness and health payoffs. You won't want to miss them.

 HAPPINESS RECIPE 6: Life Is a Gym

Trigger
3 o'clock feelings of sleepiness, fatigue, the blahs.

Response
Thirty-minute brisk walk or fifteen to twenty minutes of light exercise such as squats or jogging in place.

Payoff

Alertness, optimism, confidence, higher brain function, feelings of happiness and well-being, and relationship building!

 X-Change

If you think this 3 o'clock exercise habit would make a big difference in your life right now, download my free calendar template and mark a big red X through every day you do at least 10 minutes of exercise in the middle of the afternoon. You can gradually increase the time to 15, 20, 25, or even 30 minutes. Make a string of 7 X's to see how this habit works for you. And if you decide to make it permanent, keep that string of X's going!

> **One More Thing: The Benefits of *Vigorous* Exercise**
> Walking, squatting, and stretching are great ways to improve your physical and psychological health— true—but if you want to *substantially upgrade* your fitness, lose weight, or change how you look, you must make yourself uncomfortable. You must push yourself. But the good news is, you don't have to do it for very long.
>
> I'm talking about interval training. (Consult your doctor before trying this.) Nick Francis, a young

integrative medicine coach, taught me how interval training requires you to exert yourself intensely for short bursts of activity that raise your heart-rate to a training zone level. This is typically about 220 beats per minute, minus your age. So if you're 40 years old, it would be 220 – 40 = 180 beats per minute. You alternate these bursts of exertion with periods of recovery. Recovery is the time it takes, after you slow down, for your heart-rate to fall to 70% of your training heart rate (180 beats @ 70% = 126 beats per minute).

You can raise your heart rate in many ways, but running (can be done on a treadmill) or cycling (often in a spin class) are common. The idea is to *increase* the time you stay at your training zone heart-rate from, say, thirty seconds to two or three minutes, while you *decrease* your time recovering. As you get fitter, you will find your heart-rate dropping more rapidly, which means you're recovering faster. With some consistency, you will find you can spend more time in your high training zone and less time in your recovery zone.

Other forms of interval training include CrossFit (*http://www.crossfit.com*), which combines weightlifting, calisthenics, and mild torture into a workout so intense, it may last only six or seven minutes. Video programs like P90X and Insanity (*http://www.beachbody.com*) will definitely make you uncomfortable. My favorite nearly-daily workout is surfing a local reef that requires constant paddling, followed by intense bursts of wave riding.

The great benefit of intense interval training is that your metabolism speeds up and remains higher for hours after your workout. The training intensity produces endorphins that improve your mood and increase feelings of confidence, control, and the ability to cope with challenges. High-intensity interval training is the quickest way to improve your fitness, build muscular strength, and reshape your body.

Please comment on the thread below. Tell our Thought Rocket community what's working for you! What forms of exercise do you enjoy, how often, and what's the result? (*http://www.thoughtrocket.com/true-happiness.*)

Special Habits for Moms or Dads Who Are Domestic Engineers

If you have kids, you can adjust your exercise time to whatever's available. So if your kids take naps, use that time to try any of the exercise ideas mentioned here.

Better still, coordinate with a neighbor or friend who can bring their kids over to mind the house while your kids nap. That way, you can steal away to the gym, the pool, or the streets for a quick bout of *real* exercise.

Then return the favor for your neighbor.

 ### *Afternoon Snacks*

My favorite snack, again, is raw nuts and bits of organic dark chocolate with some sparkling water. I like Pellegrino because it makes me feel continental. If you travel or work in an office, I suggest making five little bags of nuts and chocolate and sticking them in your briefcase or purse for use as needed. Remember, the main thing is to avoid running out of energy in the afternoon. I usually need 250-300 calories to get me from lunch to dinner. Here are some other options:

- Sliced apple with almond butter
- ½ cup pumpkin seeds
- 8 oz. hot chocolate (150 calories or less, and you get chocolate too!)
- Peanut butter on celery, topped with raisins ("ants on a log")
- One stick of mozzarella string cheese, wrapped with one slice of prosciutto (Italian bacon). Eat it with three olives and you're speaking Italian.
- 3 whole grain crackers with goat cheese and tomato pesto.
- Okay, here's a favorite: ¼ cup Trader Joe's Chili con Queso with 20 baked tortilla chips (baked chips are a friend—about 220 calories.)
- And there's always the CLIF Bar option. The main thing is to stay fueled with healthy food.

Happiness Recipe 7: Making TRUE Love

Many people I coach complain about their chronic lack of work life balance. Carl was one of those people. He has a very demanding job with an endless stream of emails, conference calls, and meetings. He juggles lots of priorities. When I met him, he was caught up in a thrashing storm of competing demands from both his work and family life. He was dying inside.

Carl arrived home most nights about 7 p.m., exhausted. He would immediately tramp up to the bedroom to change out of his suit. There, the tractor beam of his desktop computer would pull him to his ever-refilling email inbox. Calls from his wife to come down to dinner at 7:30 were frequently answered by silence. Meanwhile, the Xbox raged from the family room as his two boys, aged 9 and 11, mashed buttons in a constant tide of prepubescent conflict.

When Carl did stumble down to dinner, he'd be packin' his BlackBerry. He'd lay it beside his silverware, lest any incoming message escape his attention.
His wife said Carl always tried to keep smiling and ask the

usual questions about everyone's day. He issued praise and demanded superficial obedience from his boys in a cadence that *appeared* to be engaged, but the truth was, "Behind his eyes, he was always processing his work."

As for Carl, he couldn't understand why his wife seemed perennially annoyed. Couldn't she see he had no choice? Twenty-first century work requires constant connection! Carl's assessment of himself was that he was capable enough to listen to her, be a parent, *and* keep up with his work commitments. Sigh.

Sigh, indeed. I have heard this story endlessly, as our technology-driven era erases the old rhythm of work, love and play, and replaced it with the rhythm of work, work and work. Humans are not naturally designed to thrive under conditions of relentless stress... so we don't. Thrive, that is. Instead, we cope. And much of our coping is dysfunctional. We are simply delaying our day of reckoning.

I asked Carl what would happen if nothing changed. After a week of thinking about it, he glumly replied that he would continue to be buried by stress and feel increasingly disconnected from his wife and boys. "I guess it might lead either to a break-up or a relationship I *wish* would break up."

Score one for Carl. The *recognition* of how bad things are is a key to committing to Happiness Recipe 7. Fear, in fact, tends to motivate us three to five times more than opportunity. So when your worst possible future suddenly starts to look like your *most likely* one, change becomes self-motivating.

I asked Carl whether he was ready to dedicate the time and attention to himself and his loved ones to be happy. I asked him if he was committed to his *best* future—the future that would only happen if he changed his bad habit of giving away his evenings. He asked me what was required. I said three hours. If he wasn't willing to go off the grid for three hours every night, his relationships would turn to dust.

That may sound harsh, but loving, spontaneous relationships require two regular investments. Time and attention. The problem is, the rest of your world wants your time and attention, too. Your job certainly wants it. So does the Internet, YouTube, Facebook, 24-hour news, and every advertiser and politician. We swim in a frothing sea of demands on our time and our attention. Unless we consciously choose whom to give it to—and when—we will drown in stress. Period.

How do I know? I see it every day in my work with individuals and companies. And I experience that very same pull in my own life. This is a crazy time we live in. We seem to be willing to give up everything that's essential to our happiness—our health, our loved ones, and our peace of mind—for some stress-charged, do-more-with-less job. Why? Because we are afraid that without this job, we won't be happy.

Yet we absolutely, positively know that intimate, trusting relationships are the single greatest factor in our personal happiness. We gain more joy and satisfaction from love than we do even from our own health. Love is far more satisfying than money, ambition, houses, cars, even vacations. We all know that.

We just have to stop and think about it. That's what Carl did.

As a dedicated overachiever, he put a new plan in place. He set aside thirty minutes each day, sometime between 5:00 and 6:30 p.m., to take one last whack at his email inbox, because he knew he would not be looking at it again for a long time. When driving home, he turned off news talk radio ten minutes from home and switched to what he called "Yoga" music—instrumental music that stimulates restful alpha brain waves, instead of the rapid-fire beta waves we use during our hectic, high-demand days. When Carl pulled into his garage, he left his briefcase in his car, locked, as a psychological sign that he was shifting his full attention to his loved ones.

As soon as the door opened at 7 p.m., he engaged his sons. For thirty minutes, he did whatever they wanted. He didn't go upstairs to change, because he refused to be tempted by the computer in the bedroom. (This follows the first law of habit formation: Make it easy to do what you value; make it hard to do what you don't value.) He told me that over the next few months, he ruined a suit or two playing football or Frisbee. He learned to play all kinds of crazy video games, and did an awful lot of wrestling. The main thing was, he committed to his boys' agenda. He committed to play the way *they* wanted to play.

When the family sat down to dinner, Carl had decompressed from his demands and was naturally attentive to what was being said and felt 'round the dinner table. After a few weeks, his family started a grace ritual, where each person would say one thing they were grateful for that day. Of course, sometimes the boys were silly. But often their comments led to a more interesting conversation. During dinner, the TV was off and there were no game devices at the table. No smart phones. Just full, loving presence.

After dinner, Carl started helping his wife, who also worked. Dishes, laundry, homework... Basically, the next few hours were spent working as a team in a rhythm of work, support, and communication—the kind of thing that builds trust, rapport, and friendship. About 10 o'clock Carl would fire up his computer for a final twenty to thirty minutes, to see if his work world had exploded in the three hours he had been away. Most days, it hadn't. It rarely does. Work always sucks us in with its insidious claims of urgency. Occasionally, they're warranted; usually, they're not.

How long do you think it was before Carl's family noticed the difference in him and his attentive presence? Three nights. That's right. His boys were completely engaged within 72 hours. He told me they kept asking incredulously, "Are we going to stay this way?" because the change in the family culture was so transformational.

Speaking of family culture, I will never forget the first time Stephen Covey casually said to me, "Love is a verb." I was asking him how he created such a fun culture in his family. He had nine loud children with big personalities that could have been locked in a continuous cage fight. Yet in his house it seemed like there was a party going on most of the time. That's when he told me, "Love is a verb. It doesn't just spring to life on its own. You get to create it." William James would be proud. TRUE love is created by loving action. This is what I mean by "Making TRUE Love." You *can* actually create love. Because love *is* a verb.

So that's the core of Recipe 7. It is the intentional gift of loving attention. In order to amplify the benefits of loving attention, this recipe engages two key intentions promoted by renowned "self-actualization" psychologist, Carl Rodgers, as well as two key actions that have been revealed as crucial by modern brain science.

1. Hold in your mind an *intention* of "unconditional positive regard" for your loved one. (Maybe you don't have a traditional family. In that case, whom do you trust with your secrets? Or whom do you *want* to trust?) Your inner feelings are broadcast from your brain to others' brains, whether you want them to be or not. If you are inwardly impatient, critical, or faultfinding, this will be felt by others. On the other hand, sincere feelings of "I

want you to be happy in your own special way" will also be felt.

2. Put your full attention on understanding the inner world of your loved one—without judgment and without a desire to fix the quirks and the parts that are still under construction. It's been said that our greatest hunger is to be known and to know our loved ones at the level of their hopes and dreams. We long to be genuinely valued for our uniqueness, and not criticized for our failings. So hold in your heart and mind the intention of understanding, not judging, your loved ones.

Action 1:

Touch each other lovingly. Human touch transmits energy. That is a physical fact. Loving touch is non-sexual. It communicates affection, trust, and emotional connection. Gentle, light rubbing of an arm or shoulder is one great form of loving touch between couples. Some couples and families create unspoken boundaries where touching each other seems bizarre. If this sounds like your world you can avoid freaking your partner by initiating a three-second touch. As it gets more familiar, you can increase it to pleasant handholding, hugging, or any other form of touch that creates affirming physical connection. Loving touch generates a brain chemical—oxytocin—that stimulates feelings of emotional trust, safety, and closeness. Loving touch with children can range from wrestling with boys to side-hugging with a teenager. Keep it comfortable rather than weird, but find natural ways to physically connect.

Action 2:

Communicate with transparence. Transparent communication means you share *why* you think what you think and feel what you feel. This makes you real to others. You also need to fully listen for reasons *why* your loved ones think what they think and feel what they feel. If all you talk about is *what* you think and feel, you remain a mystery. Especially if what you think and feel conflicts with your loved ones. That only creates distance and distrust. On the other hand, if you habitually share your life-logic, your story of *why* you think and feel the way you do, you build trust, friendship, and intimacy, even if your loved ones disagree with you.

We all know apparent "black sheep," who dance to the beat of a different drum. If we don't know their inner world, we tend to distance ourselves from them. If we *do* know their motives and feelings, those black sheep often become amazingly endearing. Quirky, for sure, but endearing.

So don't wait for others to ask you why you think what you think and do what you do—tell them. And gently ask them about their inner reasons for their thoughts and actions. Constantly. Be an open book, so others can read you. There is no more important habit to establish than this type of mutually transparent communication with loved ones. Three daily hours of off-the-grid time creates the space to promote transparent communication naturally.

So here is my recipe for "Making TRUE Love."

HAPPINESS RECIPE 7: Making TRUE Love

Trigger
Leaving or ending work; needing to reconnect with loved ones.

Response
1. After work, take five minutes to breathe deeply and listen to calming music to create a new inner state. Put away all electronic devices.
2. Hold your attention on your loved ones by mentally advocating for their happiness, however *they* experience it. Mindfully seek to understand *their* inner world without judgment.
3. Greet each loved one with loving touch. Make physical contact, with feeling and presence. Continue a comfortable level of touching throughout the evening. Be natural. Avoid weirdness. If they ask why you're doing it, tell them it's because you read it helps promote loving feelings in our brains. You can make it fun, even a joke. Soon it will feel completely natural.
4. Seek to know *why* each person thinks what they think and feels what they feel. Don't judge their life-logic; but also don't be afraid to occasionally prompt them to think in different ways. For instance, if someone feels bad because they failed at something that matters to them, you might ask

them what they learned from trying. Is there something positive they can take away from it? Affirm their effort or their courage. Always be suggesting, never demanding or forcing. If they don't appreciate your positive approach, don't defend yourself. Just continue giving unconditional positive regard, gently keeping up your supportiveness over weeks and months, expecting nothing in return. One of the most loving acts we can perform is to express positive belief in each other. All of us are more than we appear to be.

5. Throw yourself fully into your loved ones' activities for three hours every evening. Be fully present at dinner, helping with chores, homework, even watching a TV show. Don't multi-task. Make every act sacred by giving it your full and fun attention. Whether it's folding laundry or taking out the trash, do it mindfully.

6. Create a bedtime ritual with your partner. After you shut off the computer, agree to watch something funny on TV, or take a shower or bath together, or read side by side. Just make it your special time. To sleep well, keep your bedroom at 68 degrees, have blackout curtains, and cuddle for five minutes.

As a bonus for your health and happiness you might want to download my article "Chocolate, Sex and Sunshine" to understand how happiness is related to what you do after the lights go dim.

(http://www.thoughtrocket.com/true-happiness)

Payoff

The payoff of Making TRUE Love is your happiness. Period. With love, there is no loneliness. Without love, there is no happiness. That sums up the core of all happiness research.

High-functioning, positive, intimate relationships trigger many habits that lead to a longer, healthier, more satisfying life. And at the end of our lives, love is the one thing that matters most.

Of course, you already knew that.

TRUE Love

The music of work - life harmony is TRUE love. When love is constantly refreshed, we willingly put down our digital devices and set aside time to be fully engaged with ones we love the most. When love is TRUE it is not an act of self-discipline; rather, we can't wait to stop working, or even *playing*, to swim in our loving connections. What creates emotionally magnetic and high-functioning relationships? TRUE love.

T – Use your *Talent*, whatever you're good at, to express your love. For instance if you're good at communication and encouragement, that's how you make love. If you're good at fixing or doing things, make love through service. If you're talented at creating order and beauty or memorable experiences you can make love in that way. The secret is to offer your best most authentic gift every day to love and bless others.

R – TRUE love is its own *Reward*. We cannot pretend to love others to get what we want. That kind of fake "love" actually makes people feel worse. When we love others for their own sake, for their TRUE happiness, the feelings of love are honestly felt. There is no greater gift you can offer another.

U – Love can only be TRUE if we embrace the *Uniqueness* of our beloved. That's what happens when we fall in love. The other person is perfect to us— flaws and all. It's only later that we become judgmental and begin to focus on imperfections. Too often, we tie our happiness to changing our loved ones. This never works. We don't need anyone to change in order to be happy. We inspire others by holding high expectations for them, but allowing them to choose who they want to become. If our loved ones are mean, destructive, or selfish, we may have to love them from a safe distance, but we can still hold them in loving regard. We can pray for them and hope for them. When our own happiness is independent of the choices that others make, we are free to love them without reservation.

E – TRUE, healthy, happy love causes us to *Evolve* to our authentic, best self. This is true for both partners in a TRUE love relationship. The power of TRUE love inspires us to grow and contribute our greatest gifts.

For a powerful secret recipe for making TRUE love grow, go to *http://www.thoughtrocket.com/true-happiness* and watch Cookin' Up Some Love. It's five minutes that could change your love life.

 X-Change

Of all the habits, this one, Making TRUE Love, has the most positive impact on work - life harmony. In fact survey research confirms that having nightly dinner with family/loved ones is the most important thing we can do to increase our sense of work - life harmony.

Research also confirms that children who enjoy regular family dinners have increased confidence, higher grades, fewer behavior problems, better relationships, and everything else we want for our children. Couples who regularly enjoy fully present dinners feel more closely connected and mutually supported. They also resolve differences more easily. So break bread together!

If you are ready to commit to TRUE love right now by giving three hours a night to the people you love the most, it's time to make this recipe a habit. (If you are single, you can devote more time to your inner life, your best friends, and your extended family.) If that sounds good, download my free calendar template and make a beautiful red X through every day you complete this habit. If you start, you'll never want to stop.

Special Habit for Moms or Dad Who Are Domestic Engineers

If you're the one who's been at home with the kids all day, it's hard to refocus on being fully present with your spouse or partner. Mostly you crave relief from the relentlessness of family-raising. But if you want to grow love, you need to give just as much commitment and focused attention to your loved one as you would like given to you.

A word to the wise: when you've been in the house all day, it's easy to envy the spouse/partner who has been out in the world. Don't let that come between you.

 Dinner Recipes

Florence's Braised Chicken Breast with Lemon and Honey

I love these flavors. The sauce is lemony and jammy, and makes for a vibrant and unusual way to adorn a simple chicken breast. (Serves 4 as a main course.)

1½ Tbsp. cooking oil
4 small chicken breasts, preferably free-range, hormone and antibiotic free
Salt and freshly ground black pepper
1 large red onion, thinly sliced
8 cloves garlic, peeled, left whole
1 Meyer lemon (or other sweet lemon), cut in half and then into thick slices
¾ cup chicken stock
1½ Tbsp. Honey
2-3 sprigs thyme or marjoram, left whole

Place butter in a sauté pan over high heat. Sprinkle both sides of the chicken breasts with salt and pepper. When pan is hot, add chicken breasts. Fry for about 3 minutes a side at medium-high heat, until golden and the chicken comes away from the pan easily. (When the chicken is still raw, it will attach to the pan, so don't try to lift it too soon or it will tear.) When both sides are golden, remove from the pan and place on a plate, set aside.

Add onion to sauté pan and a sprinkle of salt, and stir-fry for 3-4 minutes, until softened. Add whole garlic cloves and stir-fry for another 2 minutes. Return chicken back to the pan together with

chicken stock, honey and thyme or marjoram.
Reduce heat to medium-low. Then cover and
simmer for 12 minutes. If you are using larger
breasts, increase the cooking time by 2-4 minutes,
depending on size. Don't overcook.

Remove the chicken breasts from pan. Season
sauce with salt and pepper to taste.

Serve chicken breasts topped with the sauce, onion,
and lemon, over rice or your favorite grain.

Note: If you cannot find sweet lemons, you may
need to increase the quantity of honey.

© Florence Quinn 2012

Heather's Herb-Crusted Grouper with Yellow Heirloom Tomato Sauce

This is a simple preparation for fish that relies on the robust flavors of the ingredients. Make sure your fish is very fresh and of high quality.

Ingredients for Fish

4 grouper filets, about 1/3 pound each
1 lemon, zested
1 Tbsp. thyme leaves
3 Tbsp. chopped flat leaf parsley
Kosher salt
2 Tbsp. high-quality extra virgin olive oil

Ingredients for Sauce

2 lbs. ripe yellow heirloom tomatoes
1 cup diced onion

3 Tbsp. extra-virgin olive oil
¼ cup chopped basil
Kosher salt and freshly ground pepper

Fish Preparation
Rub the filets with the oil, pat with herbs, lemon
zest, and kosher salt. Heat skillet for a couple of
minutes, add olive oil, and heat on high. Sauté fish
for about 2-3 minutes per side on medium-high
heat, until cooked through. (The fish should flake
easily in the center.) Don't flip the fish more than
once. Remove and serve topped with sauce.

Sauce Preparation
Cut the tomatoes into quarters. Remove the seeds
with a spoon; discard. Chop tomatoes. Heat skillet,
add olive oil, heat another minute. Add onions,
sauté over medium heat until translucent. Add
tomatoes and pinch of salt. Sauté for 8 minutes
over medium heat. Remove from heat, add
chopped basil, salt and pepper to taste.

Top herb-crusted fish with tomato sauce. Serve
with roasted potatoes and sautéed collard greens.

Florence's Stir-Fried Udon Noodles with Seared Beef & Vegetables

*Although each Asian country's food is distinct, they share
one thing in common: the rice or noodle bowl. Rice or
noodles are the foundation of the recipe. Lots of*

vegetables are then added, as well as a small piece of meat or fish and some kind of dipping sauce or soup. This is a very satisfying way to eat, as the flavors mingle in the bowl. Notice that you don't need much meat at all; it is really a garnish. So splurge on a good piece of local, grass-fed beef.

(Serves 4 as a main course.)

Beef Ingredients:
1 pound beef fillet, sirloin, or hanger steak (2 thick steaks)
1 Tbsp. sesame oil
½ Tbsp. black peppercorns, toasted
2 Tbsp. sesame seeds, toasted
1 tsp. coarse sea salt

Sauce Ingredients:
2 Tbsp. sesame oil
2 Tbsp. mirin
4 Tbsp. dark soy sauce

Stir-Fry Ingredients
2 Tbsp. cooking oil
2 Tbsp. garlic, finely chopped
2 Tbsp. fresh tender ginger, finely chopped or grated
2 large red chilies, seeded and finely sliced
1 cup scallions (spring onions), sliced 1" long
2 cups mixed mushrooms (shitake, beech, Portobello, etc.), roughly chopped

4 packets fresh Udon noodles, about 28 ounces, rinsed in cold water
4 handfuls bok choy or spinach, roughly chopped
½ cup cashew nuts, toasted

Beef Seasoning:
Coat meat with 1 tablespoon sesame oil. Using a mortar and pestle, coarsely crush peppercorns and sesame seeds; add salt. Roll fillets in the mixture and set aside on a plate.

Sauce:
In a small bowl, mix together all the ingredients of the sauce. Set aside.

Stir-Fry:
Preheat oven to 400º. Place 1 tablespoon cooking oil in frying pan over medium-high heat. When oil is hot, place meat in pan and sear for 2 minutes on each side. Transfer pan to the oven and cook for another 2-4 minutes, depending on thickness. Ideally, you want the meat to be cooked to medium-rare. (If you prefer your meat rare, you just need to sear it and skip the oven). Set aside and wrap in aluminum foil to keep warm.

While the meat is in the oven, add remaining 1 tablespoon cooking oil in a wok over high heat. When oil is hot add garlic, ginger, and red chilies. Stir-fry for 1 minute. Add spring onions and mushrooms and stir-fry for another 2-3 minutes, until mushrooms are soft and have rendered all their water. Lower heat to medium, add noodles, spinach, and prepared sauce. Cook for another minute, until noodles are hot and spinach wilted.

Distribute noodles and vegetables in four large individual bowls. Slice beef and arrange a few slices over noodles. Garnish with cashew nuts and serve immediately.
© Florence Quinn 2012

Heather's Coconut-Crusted Salmon with Cilantro-Scented Rice and Coconut Curry Sauce

<u>Cilantro Scented Rice Ingredients</u>:
¾ cup chicken stock
½ cup uncooked rice
2 Tbsp. fresh lime juice
1 tsp. zest of lime
1 Tbsp. fresh cilantro, finely chopped
½ tsp. salt

Bring water, rice, lime juice, cilantro, and salt to a boil in a small saucepan. Reduce heat to low; cover and cook 20 minutes.

<u>Coconut-Crusted Salmon Ingredients</u>:
1¼ cups shredded, unsweetened coconut
4 wild salmon filets (6 ounces each)
Salt and pepper to taste

Preheat oven to 375°. Put coconut into a freezer bag. Drop in the salmon filets one at a time, and toss to coat. Place on a lightly oiled baking sheet and season with salt and pepper. Bake for 15 minutes.

Coconut Curry Sauce Ingredients:
1 cup coconut milk
1-2 Tbsp. curry paste
1-2 Tbsp. sweet chili sauce
2 Tbsp. soy sauce
Juice of one lime
1 tsp. agave nectar
Fresh cilantro, finely chopped (for garnish)

Mix all ingredients together, except for the cilantro. Mix well, and heat until sauce is hot. Pour over the seafood. Garnish with the cilantro.

Florence's Spiced Three-Bean and Bulgur Chili

A great warming chili for these cold, foggy nights. Full of flavors and warm spices, but not hot-spicy unless you want to add more chilies. It will please vegans and non-vegans alike. (Serves 6 as a main course.)

2 Tbsp. olive oil
1 onion, roughly chopped
2 carrots, peeled, roughly chopped
1 red bell pepper, seeded, roughly chopped

4 garlic cloves, minced
4 Serrano chilies, seeded, minced
1 Tbsp. chili powder
2 tsp. ground cumin
½ cup white wine (optional)
1 28-ounce can crushed tomatoes with juices
3 cups vegetable broth or water
1 14-ounce can black beans, rinsed and drained
1 14-ounce can kidney beans, rinsed and drained
1 14-ounce can cannellini beans, rinsed and drained
½ cup bulgur
Few sprigs cilantro
6 Tbsp. plain Greek style yogurt (optional)

Heat olive oil in heavy large pot over medium heat. Add onion, carrots, and red bell pepper and sauté, stirring from time to time, until onion and carrots are soft, about 8 minutes. Add garlic, Serrano chilies, chili powder, and cumin. Sauté for another 2 minutes, stirring a couple of times.

Add wine, if using, and cook till completely reduced. Add tomatoes, vegetable broth, beans and bulgur. Bring to boil. Reduce heat to medium and cook, uncovered, until bulgur is tender and mixture thickens, stirring occasionally, about 20 minutes.

Ladle chili into bowls. Garnish with cilantro and a dollop of Greek yogurt, if using.

*Note: This chili is even better the next day. Make a
large quantity and enjoy the leftovers for 3-4 days.
You can also freeze it for up to 2 months.*

Florence's Pasta with Summer Squashes and Lemons

*This is a deceivingly simple and delicious dish. The
important thing here is to use prime ingredients: good
quality pasta; local seasonal squashes, lemons, and herbs;
and top-quality cheese. Also use a great salt like* fleur de
sel *and a good extra virgin olive oil; it'll make a
difference.*

12 ounces (320 g) farfalle, penne, or fusilli,
preferably whole wheat
1 tablespoon good quality extra virgin olive oil
1 tablespoon standard olive oil
4 cups summer squashes, cut into bite-size pieces
(see note)
1 lemon, juice
2 lemon, zest, coarsely grated
1 handful chervil, picked
1 cup parmesan, shaved
Salt and pepper, to taste

Bring a large pot of water with 1 tablespoon of
salt to a boil. Once it has reached a full boil, add
pasta and cook till *al dente*. Strain, place back in
the pot, add 1 tablespoon good quality olive oil
and keep warm while preparing the garnishes.

Place one tablespoon of olive oil in a large skillet over medium-high heat. Once hot, add squashes and a pinch of salt, and sauté for a few minutes, stirring from time to time, until the vegetables are lightly browned. They should stay crunchy.

Add sautéed squash to the pot with the warm pasta. Toss in the lemon juice and zest, chervil, and cheese. Season with a good quality salt and pepper to taste.

 Serve immediately, garnish with a few more shavings of cheese.

Notes: Pecorino or Manchego will work very well instead of Parmesan. For a different take you could also substitute Feta cheese. In the summer, look for multi-colored baby summer squashes, as they are delightful and so pretty.
© Florence Quinn 2012

Drew's Ratatouille on Polenta

2 cups Italian polenta (imported)

4 large tomatoes

4 small eggplants

4 small squash

8-10 ounces prepared tomato basil pasta sauce (this can be store-bought, but should be high-quality)

5 ounces aged Italian pecorino Romano cheese (imported)

2 Tbsp. cultured butter

5 ounces feta de chèvre (goat-cheese feta)
5 sprigs fresh rosemary
Extra virgin Italian olive oil
Fleur de sel
Freshly ground black pepper
From Drew: "For the polenta, I use an imported Italian variety. I heat the salted water to boiling in a cast iron pot and then add the pre-measured polenta to the water very slowly over a period of 2 minutes, keeping the heat high. I do this to ensure that the polenta remains silky smooth, without lumps. By the end of the 2 minutes, the polenta will be thickening rapidly. I then turn the heat to low and let it simmer, covered, for 35-40 minutes, stirring every 10 minutes or so. Once finished, I add the cultured butter and freshly grated Romano, and stir to incorporate. While stirring, I add a generous amount of *fleur de sel* and freshly ground black pepper.

"For the ratatouille, I begin by slicing, and then quartering the slices, of eggplant, squash, and tomatoes. I prefer small eggplants and squash, as their texture and flavor remain more consistent in all parts of the flesh. I spread these out on baking pans and drizzle generous amounts of extra virgin Italian olive oil on them, then sprinkle them with *fleur de sel* and freshly ground black pepper. I rub the seasonings into the vegetable flesh with my hands to ensure proper coverage, taking extra care with the eggplant, as it tends to absorb olive oil unevenly. I add several sprigs of fresh rosemary to each pan (first I lightly crush the leaves with my fingers to help release the aromatic oils).

"I then oven-roast the vegetables at 350° for 40-45 minutes or until the eggplant is lightly browned and the tomatoes have taken on a bubbly and fairly liquid consistency. About halfway through the cooking period I remove the now-blackened sprigs of rosemary. Once the vegetables have been roasted I transfer them to a bowl and add 8-10 ounces of a locally prepared tomato basil pasta sauce that I have heated in a cast iron skillet set to low. I mix the sauce and vegetables thoroughly, but gently, and season with generous amounts of *fleur de sel* and freshly ground black pepper.

"To serve, I stir the polenta to ensure a thick (but not stiff) consistency, and place a generous ladleful into the center of each plate. Then I spoon a generous amount of the roasted vegetable ratatouille mixture onto the polenta-bed, covering most of the polenta while letting some of its golden yellow remain visible. I top with crumbles of a locally crafted feta de chèvre, drizzle with extra virgin Italian olive oil, and add *fleur de sel* and freshly ground black pepper to taste."

DESSERT

Heather's Raw Chocolate Cake

     1½ cups raw walnuts, unsoaked
     Dash sea salt
     12 pitted medjool dates, unsoaked
     1/3 cup unsweetened cocoa or carob powder
     ½ tsp. vanilla extract
     ¼ cup smashed avocado
     2 tsps. water
     ½ cup fresh raspberries for garnish (optional)

Blend walnuts and salt in a food processor until finely ground. Add dates, avocado, cocoa powder, and vanilla. Process until mixture begins to stick together. Add the water and process briefly.

Transfer to a serving plate and form into a 5-inch round cake. Wipe excess spillage from plate (for presentation purposes). Chill for 2 hours. Decorate the cake and plate with fresh raspberries before serving, if desired. Covered with plastic wrap, cake will keep for three days in the refrigerator or two weeks in freezer. Yields one 5-inch cake.

Florence's Dark Chocolate Mousse

Who doesn't like a chocolate mousse? The key here is to use premium quality chocolate with a high cocoa percentage (stay away from the 'H' brand; you know what I'm talking about). This mousse is airy and light, loaded with antioxidants and contains only very healthy ingredients. This is the time to indulge and savor.

6 ounces good quality bittersweet chocolate (70-75% cacao)
⅓ cup whole milk
1 egg yolk
4 egg whites, at room temperature
2 Tbsp. sugar

Melt the chocolate in a bowl over simmering water (double boiler). Make sure the bowl does not touch the water. Stir the chocolate from time to time, until all melted. At the same time, bring milk to boiling point (but don't boil).

Take the bowl of melted chocolate off the heat and place it on the counter. Slowly pour milk over the melted chocolate, stirring with a whisk until well blended. At first it might look as if the mixture is breaking up, but continue stirring vigorously until it is smooth and shiny. Stir in the egg yolk and mix until well incorporated. Set aside.

Whip the egg whites on medium-high speed. Once they look frothy (about 30 seconds), slowly add the sugar and continue to beat until they form soft shiny peaks. Don't over-whip the whites or it will be difficult to incorporate them into the smooth chocolate. Soft, jiggly peaks are what you are looking for.

Using a whisk, mix one third of the whites into the chocolate until well combined. Then, using a spatula, gently fold in the remaining egg whites in two additions until just incorporated. Do not over-mix, as it will deflate the mousse. Transfer to a serving bowl or individual cups, and refrigerate for at least 3 hours before serving.

Note: The mousse can be kept covered in the refrigerator for 3-4 days.
© Florence Quinn 2012

Heather's Healthy Apple Crisp

4 apples (firm variety is better for baking with), cut into slices
Cinnamon
1 cup crushed nuts (almonds, pecans, and walnuts)
10 ounces of coconut milk

Spread apple slices in a square glass baking dish. Mix cinnamon with crushed nuts and sprinkle on top. Pour coconut milk over all. Bake at 425° for 30 minutes.

Florence's Almond and Coconut Cherry Clafoutis (dairy free/gluten free)

This is a take on the traditional French clafoutis— cherries in a custard that's baked and slightly broiled. It is a wonderful, easy summer treat. By replacing all-purpose flour with almond flour, and the butter with coconut oil, you infuse it with a nice nutty flavor and make it extra healthy.
(Serves 6.)

> 1⅓ pound cherries, pitted
> 1 Tbsp. sugar
> ⅓ cup powdered sugar
> 5 Tbsp. coconut oil, at room temperature
> 2 large eggs
> 2 Tbsp. coconut cream
> 1 pinch salt
> 1 cup almond flour/meal or finely ground almonds
> 1 pinch powdered sugar, for garnish (optional)

Lightly oil a 7" square baking dish using some coconut oil and set aside. Preheat oven to 375°.

Place pitted cherries in medium-size saucepan with one tablespoon sugar. Bring to a simmer and cook for 5 minutes, stirring once or twice. The cherries will have slightly softened and given out some of their juices. Pour cherries and their juices into the prepared baking dish.

Using a mixer, whisk powdered sugar and coconut oil until smooth, about 2 minutes. Add eggs, coconut cream, almond meal, and salt. Whisk until smooth and well blended. It should be fairly thick. Pour mixture over the cherries in baking dish.

Bake for about 25 minutes, until custard is firm and the top is golden brown. Allow to cool. This dessert is best served slightly warm or at room temperature within a few hours of baking. Dust with powdered sugar (if using) just before serving.

Note: You can replace the cherries with berries such as raspberries, blackberries, or blueberries. In that case, you don't need to cook them first, just throw them raw into the bottom of the baking dish.
© Florence Quinn 2012

Banana Bread French Toast

I'll leave you with an astonishingly delicious dessert. I came across it at the Flaming Buoy restaurant in Key West. And yes, it is Banana Bread French Toast. I've had it for breakfast once, but its real delight is as a dessert, served with homemade vanilla ice cream or some out-of-this-world hazelnut gelato. The key is to get the edges of the banana bread slightly crispy, and to drizzle, rather than soak, the banana toast in all-natural maple syrup. This isn't an everyday dessert. It's a special occasion food that deserves highly mindful tasting and a slow, good chew. It is definitely "happy" food.

Monkey Banana Bread

When I was 7, I wanted to be a monkey. I had a stuffed chimp named Zip that I took everywhere. At school, I played on the monkey bars for hours and ate lots of bananas. An intervention from my mother helped snap me out of being Monkey Boy, but I never got over my taste for bananas. This banana bread is so delicious, a monkey would steal it. Hence its name.

<u>Ingredients for Bread</u>
2 large organic eggs
¾ cups raw sugar
1 cup smashed bananas (about 3 bananas, very ripe)
1¾ cups all-purpose flour
1/3 cup buttermilk
1 Tbsp. canola oil
1 Tbsp. vanilla extract
2 tsps. baking powder
½ tsp. baking soda
½ tsp. salt

Beat eggs and sugar in a bowl with an electric mixer until light and thick (usually 4-5 minutes). Mix in buttermilk, oil, smashed bananas, and vanilla. Sift flour, baking soda, baking powder, and salt over the batter and mix until fully blended.

176

Pour the batter in a lightly greased 8 X 4-inch bread pan. Bake bread in preheated oven at 325°. Bake until the bread turns golden brown (usually about 45 min.-1 hour) and a toothpick inserted into the loaf's center comes out fairly clean, not gooey. Remove the bread and carefully pop it onto a cooling rack. Let it cool for a while. Okay, almost there...

Ingredients for French Toast Mix
3 eggs
1 tsp. vanilla extract
2 Tbsp. butter
3 Tbsp. condensed milk
Pure maple syrup for drizzling

Thoroughly mix the eggs, vanilla, and condensed milk. Melt butter on a griddle or in a large skillet or frying pan. Slice banana bread about 1 inch thick. Submerge each slice in the egg mixture then place it on the skillet and cook until the under edge is slightly crisp. Turn and cook on the other side. Don't overcook. You just want to be sure the outer edges are golden crisp.
Drizzle (don't pour) Vermont or Canadian pure maple syrup on the toast. Serving size is one slice with premium vanilla ice cream or hazelnut gelato.

Now... get a forkful of the French toast and some ice cream. Close your eyes and make a wish. Call the paramedics to revive you. (This may cause a trance of ecstasy. At least it did to Monkey Boy.)

Smart Pleasure

Pleasure that hurts us in the long run results in unhappiness. Pleasure that *doesn't* hurt us leads to happiness. I call that smart pleasure. Smart pleasure is not about self-denial or withholding our enjoyment of things. Quite the opposite. Smart pleasure is about *fully enjoying* the things we love the best. But only while their pleasure-giving quotient is at its highest.

When we enjoy pleasure in small, intense doses, we extract the most enjoyment from rich food and other indulgences, while doing ourselves the least harm. That's because much of our sense of pleasure comes from the brain chemical, dopamine. Dopamine calms and de-stresses us. It lifts our mood and makes us optimistic. But dopamine is a fickle friend. Our pleasure receptors quickly get used to nice things and stop squirting dopamine. Pretty soon, pleasure starts to fade.

This is especially true with food. When we bite into something delicious, like a moist piece of dream chocolate cake, our pleasure center ignites like fireworks on the Fourth of July. On the second bite we get a nice, bright Roman candle of pleasure. By our third bite, it's down to a happy little sparkler. After that, we scarf the rest on automatic pilot. We're getting the calories, the sugar, and the fat, but not the pleasure.

The trick is to grab all the pleasure we can while the dopamine is gushing, and then stop.

When it comes to rich and decadent food, for example, enjoy it thoroughly. But follow the Three-Bite Rule. Here's how. Focus your full sensory apparatus on the high-pleasure food. Smell its aroma. Study its colors and textures. Visually taste it before you dive in. Then close your eyes as you take the first small bite. Chew it slowly. Feel the textures against your tongue, teeth, and the roof of your mouth. Describe all the taste sensations to yourself. After you slowly swallow, take a slow, deep breath and reset for bite number two. Repeat for bite three. Then retire the fork. That's all you need. You really won't get much more pleasure from eating more. Guilt, maybe, but not pleasure.

Happiness Recipe 8: Unplug, Rest, Recharge

Do you believe there's a strong connection between sleep and success? Well, consider this. Some years ago, I was consulting for Doug, a CEO who decided he didn't have enough hours in the day to run his large investment firm. So he spent two years "training" himself to sleep only four hours a night. I left about one year into his experiment, but ran into him on a plane about three years later and asked how he was doing. He told me his business had gone bankrupt. When I asked him why, he said it was from "lack of sleep." He told me he started a cycle of making stupid decisions and not listening to his team. It got worse and worse, as he continued to fall asleep at the wheel. Eventually, he drove his company off a cliff.

Doug is not alone. A lot of us are asleep at the wheel. Never before have so many people slept so little. Electric light was a world-changing invention, but one of its unintended side effects has been exhaustion. It has allowed us to ignore the natural rhythms of sunrise and sunset by which our ancestors set their inner clocks.

Research suggests that the average adult slept about nine hours a night in 1900. Today the average is closer to 6.5 hours. That's a whopping 30% less sleep. And it's killing us.

The strong evidence is that chronic sleep deprivation weakens our immune system, makes us moody, impairs our memory, accelerates aging, and retards our ability to solve problems. If that's not enough, fatigue makes us fat. Well, maybe not directly, but research shows that when we are tired from lack of sleep, our body craves energy so it tries to make it up through calories. As wellness expert Dr. Daniel Friedland told me, lack of sleep makes us slow, sick, and stupid.

Yes, stupid. Ample research reveals that we need sleep to make learning stick. Students who study longer hours by pulling all-nighters make more mistakes on tests than students who study less, but get seven hours or more of sleep before tests. It seems our brain continues to work during sleep, sorting new information and connecting it to things we already know in ways that give us new insights.

Sleep does even more than make us smart and healthy. It also fuels our happiness. The recharge we get from sleep stimulates our gratitude and optimism. Restful sleep strengthens our resilience to setbacks, and enables us to be mindful and to seek social connection. Sleep even makes us feel sexy and interested in intimacy.

The bottom line is this—if you want your sixteen hours of

daily wakefulness to rock, you should become a champion
sleeper for the other eight hours. (Most research confirms
that typical humans need between seven and eight hours of
quality sleep to function well and enjoy full health. Yes,
this means you.)

Sleep is such an important habit, I am going to offer 21
general tips before I lay out the recipe. Everyone is a little
different, so you can experiment with these tips and see
what works best for you.

Create a sleeper's paradise:
1. Your bedroom should be set aside for sleep and sex
   only. Most experts suggest no TV, no computer, no
   iPads, no iPhones—take your bedroom completely
   off the grid.
2. Use low-wattage light sources. Keep your bedroom
   lights low even when they are switched on. Once
   they are turned off, keep them off. Use a flashlight
   if you have to get up during the night.
3. Total darkness. The biological stimulus for sleep is
   darkness. This is what triggers the release of
   melatonin, the brain chemical that promotes
   drowsiness. Make sure you go outside every day
   before noon for ten minutes, and let natural
   sunlight hit your eyes. This will shut down
   melatonin production during the day and reset
   your internal timer. To create absolute darkness in
   your bedroom, use blackout curtains or an eye
   mask (you'll look like a movie star). Cover up any
   alarm clocks that have an illuminated face, and get

rid of night-lights. Even those tiny LED lights on electronic devices can create a lot of unwanted ambient light.

4. Keep your bedroom temperature at about 68 degrees, as your body sleeps most restfully when it's cooler. Many people prefer temperatures even cooler than 68, but if you get too cold it will also wake you up. Wearing lightweight socks can help prevent your toes from icing over.

Adopt a sleep-promoting lifestyle:

5. Determine how caffeine-sensitive you are. As we age, most of us metabolize caffeine more slowly, so drinking coffee or other caffeine carriers after 2 p.m. can disturb our sleep. Everyone is different, so pay attention to the effect caffeine has on you.

6. Exercise daily, but do it during the day if possible. Exercise promotes restful sleep; however, vigorous exercise in the evening tends to rev you up, making sleep more elusive.

7. Avoid too much alcohol, especially close to bedtime. I know it may help you get to sleep, but the evidence shows it prevents you from descending into the most restful sleep cycles.

8. Pay attention to whether spicy foods irritate your stomach. An active stomach will keep you awake. (Read on to see the benefits of a proper bedtime snack.)

9. Avoid drinking too much liquid at least two hours before bed, and make sure to empty your bladder right before bed. This will minimize nighttime trips

to the bathroom.

10. If you feel it helps, take a melatonin supplement an hour or two before bedtime. Studies show melatonin helps most people fall asleep, stay asleep, and sleep more restfully. Our bodies produce tons of melatonin when we're teenagers and can win Olympic medals for endurance-sleeping. Unfortunately, as we get older we produce less and less of this chemical friend.

Engage in sleep rituals:

11. Strive for a bedtime between 10 and 11 p.m. Evidence suggests our body's most powerful recharging takes place before 1 a.m. (This includes our kinetic energy system, which recharges our muscular, nervous, and chemical systems.)

12. Fifteen minutes of mindful stretching or a brief yoga routine, about an hour before sleeping, helps relax tense muscles, reduces stress, and centers your mind.

13. Stop all work at least ninety minutes before bedtime. Relax your mind. If you are watching TV, don't watch upsetting newscasts or stimulating suspense shows. Comedies or uplifting, fully resolved dramas are best.

14. As you get ready for bed, light up a scented candle strong enough to change the dominant scent. Lavender is very relaxing to most people. (Make sure you extinguish the candle before you fall asleep, or you may be awakened by the local fire department.)

15. Take a hot bath. After I give a lengthy speech or workshop, I often have muscle soreness, which can be a sleep killer. I can also get emotionally keyed up from all the excitement. A hot bath, as hot as I can stand it, relaxes my muscles and raises my body temperature. You see, when we overheat our body (not scald it), it fights to lower its temperature back to normal. As it does, our internal cooling system makes us sleepy. A couple of warnings, though. A super-hot bath may not be healthy if you have a heart condition, so talk to your doctor if you want to try this. Second, if you take a hot bath and turn out the lights, you might fall asleep in the tub! Careful.

16. Read something inspiring or spiritually/emotionally enriching for twenty minutes before sleeping. Better yet, listen to it in audio format. Thousands of podcasts, dramas, and audio books are now available on websites and places like iTunes U. Many are free. Listening can be far more relaxing than reading. Audio books and podcasts are also a great option if you wake up at night and have trouble going back to sleep, because they don't require light.

17. Pre-program your dreams. New research on dream therapy confirms that many people can reduce disturbing thoughts and nightmares by taking three minutes before bedtime to tell their brains what to dream about. Of course, you'll want to avoid telling your brain what *not* to think, because that *creates* the very images you are trying to escape. Instead,

visualize what you'd *like* to think about, such as relaxing on a beach of pink sand.

18. Reduce nighttime worries by keeping a "worry" journal. Obsessive worrying is often amplified by a fear that you'll forget what you're worrying about. I know it sounds crazy, but your emotions try to keep what's important to you at the center of your attention. So if you're worried about losing your job, your emotions will not let you forget about that fear. Or if you suddenly remember a tax bill that's due, your emotions will fret over it until it's dealt with. Often, you can calm down your obsessive emotions by writing down your worries. The worry list relieves your short-term memory of its need to keep reminding you of your problems, allowing you to "let them go." So keep a worry journal by your bed, and if you find yourself on a worry treadmill, make a short note of the worry, release it, and go to sleep.

19. Keep a "great idea" journal handy, too. Why? Dream-storming (unconscious brain-storming) is a great problem-solving tool. It works like this. Let's say you're trying to decide whether to look for a new job or where to go on vacation—any decision that has complicating factors. Before you go to sleep, ask yourself a question beginning with the word "how." "How can I be smart about looking for a new job?" or "How can I make the best decision about my vacation?" Our brains love "how" questions because these require synthesizing lots of information from our life experience, our skills,

and our judgment, in order to conjure up creative solutions. This is one of your brain's highest uses. And I believe when we give our brain a chance to run, it puts on its Nikes and hits the track. My own experience with dream-storming has been nothing short of life-changing. I've found that if I don't wake up and write an idea down, though, one of two things happens. Either I obsess about the solution for the rest of the night, which ruins my sleep, or I forget about it by morning. A word of caution: not all dream-storms are great ideas, so don't treat them as mystical. They come from *your brain.*

20. Don't watch TV or read on a backlit screen during the night. The intense light from an iPad, TV, or computer will arouse your wakeful state.

21. Cuddle. Yes, cuddle. If you are in a committed and trusting relationship, embracing in a gentle cuddle for six minutes will spark your brain to produce oxytocin, the brain chemical associated with emotional bonding and safety. This neurotransmitter has a calming effect on your nervous system, reduces cortisol, and generally amplifies feelings of well-being.

Well, there you have it. My 21 science-based tips on getting a good night's sleep. Now I am going to give you my recipe for solidifying this habit in your life. It's called Unplug, Rest, and Recharge. You will notice I include some ideas not listed in the previous tips. These are things that work for me. Each of us needs to create and re-create sleep habits that are uniquely effective for us. Some things might work well for a while, but then lose their efficacy. So find your own best sleep rituals. Start with this recipe, then tinker with it as you would any good recipe. Remember, sleeping should be pleasurable.

 HAPPINESS RECIPE 8: Unplug, Rest, and Recharge

Trigger
One hour before bedtime—usually 9-9:30.

Response
1. Go to the bedroom and turn off all overhead lights, leaving only one low-wattage nightstand light on. Light a scented candle.
2. Do ten minutes of Instant Yoga, watching the video (*http://www.thoughtrocket.com/true-happiness*) of ten poses that stretch and center you. You may prefer your own ten minutes of mindful stretching. That's fine. Just loosen up.
3. Take a hot bath for 7-10 minutes, while reflecting on what you're grateful for or listening to some inspiring ideas from a podcast. (Sometimes I listen to calming "nature" music.)
4. Eat a small 200-calorie snack. (I especially like half a banana with almond butter—food is my friend.)
5. Do a Flourish Journal entry. Flourish is a simple exercise popularized by Dr. Martin Seligman.

Simply ask yourself what are three things you did well that you enjoyed today. Write the answers down. In 21 days, you will see a pattern of things you do when you're flourishing. These are the things you want to do more of. This exercise is a great way to get your mind in a state of affirming rest as you turn the lights out. It really centers me.

6. Take ten deep, cleansing breaths as you lay flat on your back. Breathe in through your nose, out through your mouth. Focus your attention on your breath. Note: many people have trouble sleeping because of shallow breathing or mouth breathing. Nasal strips, the kind football players use that stick over your nose and lift your nostrils slightly, can be a remarkable help. They can open your nasal passages and allow much more oxygen to your brain. (The most common brand is Breathe Right® Strips.)

7. If you are lucky enough to have someone special to cuddle with, do so.

8. If you awaken during the night, use the strategies listed in the 21 tips. Have a flashlight handy. Keep a worry journal and a dream-storming journal by your bedside. Have your audio player handy to listen to something, if you can't resume your sleep. Try meditative breathing. (Concentrating on your breathing should *bore* you back to sleep! At least, it works for me.)

Payoff

Regular good sleep will give you more optimism, greater

concentration, a deeper desire to socialize, more patience, a more open mind, greater health and energy, and a more powerful life force. Sleep will turn up the volume on your best self.

 X-Change

If you want to make a new sleep habit a permanent part of your lifestyle, choose the tips that most apply to you. Don't be afraid to step out of your comfort zone and light a candle or take a bath, but choose a ritual you are willing to try for at least a week. Every night that you do the habit, mark your calendar with a big X. Once you have established a ritual that you want to stick with, try it for 21 days, marking each successful evening with an X. Remember, the X's do not indicate whether or not your sleep was great. You are simply tracking whether or not you are sticking to your sleep habit. (If you start tracking your sleep *quality*, you may create performance anxiety that actually interferes with your sleep.)

Good, restful sleep is a universal quest. If you have any suggestions or specific sleep strategies that work for you, please join us at *http://www.thoughtrocket.com/true-happiness* and tell us. I am convinced our whole world would work better if we all got a little more sleep.

Special Habit for Moms, Dads, and Pet Lovers
I hate to tell you this, but there is strong

evidence to suggest that sleeping with your pets or children is a major source of sleep disturbance. So make a bed for your children or pets *next to yours,* if you wish to keep them close. But give yourself some personal space on your mattress.

 ### *Bedtime Snacks*

The idea that bedtime snacks are bad for you is a myth. In fact, 100-200 calories before bed has been shown to keep your metabolism at an optimal level for sleep. Of course, not all bedtime snacks are good. You should avoid spicy food, citrus, and high-sugar foods. I know, that eliminates a lot of your favorite "recreational" food. But here are some healthy bedtime snacks that may help you sleep a bit better.

Florence, my Swiss chef nutritionist friend, suggests her mother's favorite sleep-friendly snack—warm milk and a dollop of honey. Milk and other dairy products contain tryptophan, an amino acid that helps your body slip off to sleep by stimulating both melatonin and serotonin production. If you can digest warm cow's milk, go with that and add no more than a teaspoon of honey. If lactose upsets you, use almond milk. Almonds promote sleep and muscle relaxation. Florence recommends almonds, dried cherries, and a bit of honey as another great bedtime snack (cherries actually contain melatonin).

Other favorites of mine are:

- 1 slice of whole grain toast with almond butter or honey and 4 oz. of milk
- Half a banana with almond butter
- According to the experts at WebMD, light dairy and carbohydrates with tryptophan are good bedtime snacks. They suggest:
    - Small pieces of cheese, along with oat or whole grain crackers (anytime cheese is a recommended food, I try to take advantage of it).
    - A small bowl of hot oatmeal with milk

Quick, simple, light, and basic—that's the idea.

Our Pursuit of Happiness

Now that I've "tucked you in" for the night, it's time to say goodbye. For now. But first I'd like to circle back to something I said at the beginning of the book. That is, science *does* know the secret of happiness. I'm not kidding. For over fifty years, social scientists have been searching for the common denominators in people who enjoy the longest lives, greatest health, best financial security, most fulfilling work, happiest marriages, and deepest life satisfaction. And they've found them! So we no longer need to treat happiness as if it's some elusive feather in the wind, always to be chased, never to be caught.

We just need to develop some new habits, like the ones I've been suggesting here.

Many times in this book I've referred to scientific research. There's one more study I'd like to mention before we go. It's an experiment on impulse control that was conducted by Dr. Walter Mischel. Mischel tested a group of four-year-olds' ability to resist eating marshmallows for fifteen minutes. Their motivation for waiting? The promise of a bigger reward. Now, as you know, a four-year-old's self-discipline is pretty limited. Many went for the marshmallows. But some did not. Over a twenty-year period, Mischel's team found that those four-year-olds who controlled their impulses were significantly happier and more successful later in life than those who caved into temptation. It turns out that people who regularly act on "feel-good" impulses are not indeed happier. This seems kind of obvious. Our prisons are jammed with people who have poor impulse control. *Self*-control is crucial.

But self-control is only part of what leads to TRUE happiness. Many people who have supreme self-control are *also* miserable, trapped in endless cycles of achieving goals that others have set. To foster TRUE happiness, self-control must be *self-directed*. It can't come from trying to please others or gain social approval.

Rather, self-direction comes from forming a vision of your future self. A self-vision. Do you have one? Can you describe your most fulfilling life as you would like to live it over the next ten years? Can you write down what you would like to have accomplished ten years from now that will bring you the most joy? Can you paint a picture of your most fulfilling relationship ten years from now? Can you see a tapestry of your most valued contributions, your best work, and your most engaging pursuits? This ability to create and describe your future self has a very high correlation with TRUE happiness.

The reason is simple. Every day, we have choices to make. Nearly every choice has a larger consequence. It either takes us closer to our best health, best work, best relationships, best lifestyle, best thinking, and best character, or it takes us further away. To know, minute-to-minute, what our best choice is, we must have a vision to focus on. A self-vision.

Now I don't want to confuse or misguide you here. A self-vision is not a Vision Board taped to your refrigerator, or a post on your Facebook profile. These dream boards are too often filled with pictures of a fantasy lifestyle—lookin' hot and livin' large. A self-vision is different. It is rooted in having clear values and deeply held priorities. It is based on being crystal clear on what's important to you. As Stephen Covey taught me, our self-vision is not about our future *net* worth, but our future *self*-worth.

My mountain climbing partner, Chris Osorio, puts it this way: "The purpose of life is to become and contribute your authentic best... to be and do your best... as you define it." That's it. That's what it means to be TRUE to yourself. And this process never ends.

So what's the secret of life? It's simple. Invest wisely in your future self. The self *you* will most admire. By investing wisely, I mean focusing your time, energy, discipline, mind, and body toward becoming the best version of you. This is TRUE happiness. When you have a self-vision, there is no such thing as a neutral choice. Every choice either takes you closer to TRUE happiness, or takes you away from it. So don't waste your time doing things you neither value nor enjoy.

One more thing.

Always remember that you are not your life circumstances. There is one thing I can guarantee: your life will not turn out exactly the way you envision it. There are way too many things we cannot control. The biggest body blows in our lives—death, sickness, divorce, business failure, unemployment—usually happen by surprise. We can't control our life circumstances—not entirely—but what we *can* control is who we are and who we become. That's what a self-vision is all about.

Invest in yourself. Always.

May the force of TRUE happiness fill your life.

As I enter the final lap on the running-track of my life, I'm dedicating myself to helping others find their best path to TRUE happiness. Every week, I publish a new habit of happiness related to 16 essential areas of human experience. You can find these habits by going to http://www.thoughtrocket.com/true-happiness. You can also join a growing community of people who want more than the random circumstances that modern life provides. They want to make "their" difference. Please join us.

ACKNOWLEDGEMENTS

I especially want to thank Florence Quinn and Heather Fleming for their enthusiastic guidance and ideas on nutrition and recipes. My son Adam, the fun boy, who shows me how to do serious work and have very serious fun every day. My son Nick, a Master's candidate in kinesiology and sports psychology, who keeps me up to date on the growing connection between exercise and well-being. My son Drew, an amazing "slow food" expert who makes great food every day while he works at a demanding job and holds his family in a loving embrace. My nurse daughter Natassia, who taught me anything is possible when it comes to learning really hard subjects if it empowers you to do what thrills your soul. My yoga diva, fashion entrepreneur daughter, Nicole who makes any job a happy one. And to my wife Debbie, who reads my mind as well as my manuscripts. She makes everything she touches better.

As for the book, I want to thank my super-talented editor Andy Wolfendon, whose insight, talent, and suggestions make all ideas better. To Jeannie Foy, my production assistant who never tires of doing more and telling me when I am on track. To my researcher and Thought Rocket blogger, Chelsea Batten, who diligently finds the latest published research and makes it readable. And to Ted Ehr, Paul Schwartz, Michael Johnson, Marcelo Radulovich, Maruxa and Dennis Murphy, Kris Hedberg and Steve Clayback who together form a talented team of practical idealists who are crazy enough to think we can all be happier through positive action.

RECOMMENDED

Happy Career, Healthy Life

Over the past 30 years that I've been helping people excel at their work I've seen the radical toll our modern way of working has taken on *your* happiness. Doing more with less has meant taking more out of *you*.

Today many of my clients, even those who are top executives, live in survival mode. It's such an issue that I created an online course called "Turn Your Superpower Into Your Career" to teach people how to start careers independently from their current jobs. I am committed to helping people think beyond the fear of losing their paycheck. If you're interested go to **Turn Your Superpower Into Your Career** (*http://www.thoughtrocket.com/courses/*) and take control of your future. And join our community at *http://www.thoughtrocket.com/true-happiness* for a daily dose of positive action.

Human Change and Forming Habits

One Small Step Can Change Your Life by Bob Maurer—The best book I ever read on how human beings actually escape from bad habits and reinvent their lives. Bob Maurer is a kind genius who makes change easy, friendly, and enjoyable.

Rip It Up by Dr. Richard Wiseman—A radically practical approach to changing anything. Wiseman is something of a wild man—a performer and promoter of serious ideas made simple.

Human Performance

For training in the science of human energy, The Human Performance Institute is the gold standard. It offers many off-site options, including a new online course and several inspiring books such as *The Power of Full Engagement* and *The Power of Story* (*http://www.hpinstitute.com*).

Happiness

Authentic Happiness by Martin Seligman—Still *the* classic book on happiness. Great website as well (*http://www.authentichappiness.org*).

Emotional Longevity by Norman Anderson—Research secrets from the National Institutes of Health on what makes life worth loving.

The Happiness Advantage by Shawn Achor—Why happiness and work go together.

Brain Science

Supersmarthealth.com is the brainchild of my friend and colleague Dr. Daniel Friedland, M.D. He has an inspiring way of connecting neuroscience, emotional intelligence, and evidence-based medicine in practical ways to optimize day-to-day living.

Mind Sight by Daniel Siegel, M.D.—Eye popping, mind-bending science and useful ideas to understand and train your brain.

Spark by John Ratey—Inspiring research on the impact of exercise on our brains and our lives.

Nutrition
Culinary Intelligence: The Act of Eating Healthy (And Really Well) by Peter Kaminsky—Uncommon sense about food, health, and pleasure.

http://www.AboutFood.biz—Stay up to date on Florence Quinn's world cooking tours and new flavor-rich recipes. She is adventurous, yet practical. Very French-Swiss.

"Conscious Nutrition: Eat. Live. Thrive."—Great leading-edge advice for people serious about eating well to feel well. Find it at *http://www.consciousnutrition.com*.

You On a Diet by Mehmet Oz and Michael Roizen—Simple ways to manage your glucose, your body, your feelings, and your weight.

TheYummyLife.com—Monica Matheny is a mom who knows how to make easy, yummy food you don't see every day. Different. Delicious.

Work That Makes You Happy and Fulfilled
Save the World and Still Be Home For Dinner by Will Marré—The formula we discovered during the American Dream Project about how real people work, love, and play, every day.

INDEX OF FOOD RECIPES

NOTES

About the Author

Will Marré is CEO and founder of the ThoughtRocket Innovation Studio, a new online human development platform providing up-to-the-minute leadership research and courses detailing what successful, happy people are doing to thrive in the 21st century. Will Marré is also the cofounder of the Covey Leadership Center where he brought the *Seven Habits of Highly Effective People* to millions of executives and managers worldwide. Will served on the advisory board of the Human Performance Institute, founded the American Dream Project, and is an Emmy award-winning writer of a public television learning documentary. For more information, please visit *http://www.thoughtrocket.com.*